Amelia's Daughter

Amelia's Daughter

Susan Evans McCloud

KenningHouse
Newport Beach, California

First printing, August 1982
Printed in the United States of America.

KenningHouse
Newport Beach, California.

Acknowledgments

S pecial thanks to the Utah Historical Society for their kind cooperation in research; to Dr. Jack Johnson and Gregory Seal for their willing and interesting professional counsel; to Jennie, Jared, and Heather McCloud for their timely support and invaluable service; and to James—whose book, in a special way, this is.

S.E.M.

To my MOTHER —
  whose story this is . . .
and ought to have been

It is strange but true; for truth is always strange—stranger than fiction.

—Byron

Be of good cheer;
You've fallen into a princely hand,
Fear nothing.
SHAKESPEARE

————————————————————————————— 1

The conductor called out "Elmwood," and Julia lurched to her feet, making her way through the crowded streetcar, reaching the doors just as they folded open with a hiss, seeming to suck her out and into the cool Chicago evening. She took a deep, grateful breath as the doors hissed shut again and the streetcar rumbled away. It was cool for April. She hugged her light coat about her as she turned. Perhaps she would take a moment and buy a candy bar at the drugstore on the corner.

She drew in her breath and stood, staring. The drugstore was there; there was a drugstore on every corner in this part of Chicago. But it wasn't the right drugstore. And the letters on the signpost beneath the dim street lamp read "Oakwood." Julia knew, with a sinking feeling, that she was lost.

How had she heard "Elmwood" instead of "Oakwood" when the conductor slurred out the name? She should have listened more carefully. A little shiver crept over her. The night was so dark, and the street so deserted and still. A small town girl alone in the big city had no business getting off at the wrong stop. She glanced at her wrist watch. It was nine twenty-five. She should have gone home when the manager told her and not stayed to help with inventory. Oh well, there was nothing she could do about it now. Perhaps Elmwood was only the next block down. Most of the streets in the area ended with *wood*. It couldn't be far.

Julia started to walk. Her heels made sharp, staccato sounds on the pavement. Too loud; too conspicuous. There were so many shadows! She clutched her purse and counted the storefronts she passed, all locked and darkened for the night.

She heard the car before she saw it. It had pulled alongside the curb, keeping pace with her. She tried to walk faster, but stumbled awkwardly over a crack, blushing with embarrassment, glad for the dark.

"Need a ride, miss? I'm sure I'm going your way." The voice was young and smooth and openly suggestive.

Julia hazarded a glance. The man looked young, and his grin had an indolent air. His arm rested easily along the opened window. Strong, sinewy fingers tapped a light, impatient rhythm against the door. A sensation crawled over Julia's skin, leaving her cold. She averted her eyes and walked with more purpose now. Lazily the car kept pace.

"Sweetheart." The voice was more intimate now, more persuasive. "A looker like you ain't safe on the streets alone. Let me take you home. It's no trouble. . . honest."

The nerve of the man! Did he really think she believed she'd be safer with him, in a car, than alone on the streets? *I'll take my chances,* she thought, angry now. She turned to the man, hoping her fear didn't show.

"Thanks anyway, but I don't have far," she lied.

He shrugged. The tapping fingers kept up their rhythm. The long, quiet car began to pull ahead. A dozen yards, two dozen yards, still hugging the curbing. Julia realized she was shaking. What if the dark young man had stopped the car? What if he'd opened the door and . . .

She shook her head. Here was the corner, the signpost. Julia hardly dared look. *Please be Elmwood,* she prayed. But the sign, when she looked, spelled *Lindenwood* with long, slender letters. Lindenwood. What should she do? One more block. She'd walk one more block. And then . . .

The next corner would be Elmwood. It had to be. She couldn't have misjudged that far! She held her head high and walked, counting the sharp, trim clicks of her own steps. This was a long block, burgeoning with shadow. It would be all right. The next street would be Elmwood. Julia began to hum a tune under her breath. Then she saw the car pulled up to the curb. Sitting dark and motionless, half a block ahead. Waiting for her. A hard fear gripped at her stomach. She closed her eyes and whispered a little prayer.

When she opened them again, she saw the figures. Had they been there before? Two people, walking only yards ahead of her. She quickened her own steps. A man . . . and a woman! She almost sobbed in relief, then broke into a gentle run.

The man heard her first and turned as she grabbed his arm.

"Excuse me . . . but, do you mind? Could I walk with you?"

He was young. A sparkle quickly replaced the confusion in his eyes.

"I'm not the guy to refuse a feminine appeal. We've room for one more. Margie, meet . . ." He paused and smiled encouragingly. Julia felt awkward and embarrassed. She took a deep breath.

"You don't understand. Do you see that car up there? He's waiting for me."

"A tiff with your boyfriend, huh?" The young man laughed, an easy, gentle laugh.

"No, no!" There was something in Julia's voice and face now that stopped him. He patted the small white hand that clung to his arm.

"I'm sorry. It took me awhile. You're all right now. When he sees you with us, he'll take off."

They drew closer to the big car. She could see the fingers tapping against the door.

"You okay? Just look straight ahead. Margie, say something!"

Margie giggled. "I say, Nolan, an evening with you is never a dull affair."

They all laughed then; they passed the parked car laughing. When Julia looked back, the car had already turned and was moving down the street in the opposite direction. She sighed once in relief.

"Oh, thank you," she breathed.

"My pleasure." Nolan raised a quizzical eyebrow.

"I know. I shouldn't be walking the streets alone." Julia hesitated, wondering how to explain. "You see, I'd been working late. I took the streetcar and got off at what I thought was my stop, but it wasn't."

"So you're lost. Oh, dear." Margie sounded genuinely concerned. "Well, Nolan's car is just around the corner. You can trust him to take you home." She crinkled her mouth into a mischievous grin. "Though he probably looks as much the wolf as that man in the car did."

Julia smiled. She felt warm and at ease with these two young people.

"Ignore her, ignore her. Wishful thinking, eh, Margie? Where to, young lady?"

"Elmwood," Julia replied.

"Elmwood. That isn't far. Now, miss . . ."

Julia felt herself color. "Oh, I'm sorry. I'm Julia Wilde."

"And you're not from Chicago." Nolan's eyes, though sparkling with fun, were kind.

"No, obviously not." Julia couldn't help laughing. "Freeport. A small town a hundred or so miles west. I'm only here for two weeks on a training program."

They reached the corner and turned.

"Here's Nolan's car." Margie waited for Nolan to unlock the door, then slid quickly across the seat. "We can all three fit in front." She smiled at Julia, who climbed in gratefully beside her. "What are you training for? Something exciting?" Margie asked.

"Not really. Just manager for a Bata Shoe chain."

Nolan whistled low. "Sounds impressive to me," he said.

"I'll say, when compared to waiting tables at Streepies." Margie wrinkled up her nose distastefully.

Julia smiled. "You're both kind. I don't know what I'd have done without you."

"Well, now, a manager ought to make a pretty good wage, even in war time." Nolan's voice held an appraising note.

"Nolan, you leave her alone," Margie scolded. "You'll see I was right," she cautioned, smiling over at Julia. "Nolan loves to prey on unsuspecting females."

They both laughed, and Nolan handed across his card.

"I'm a salesman," he explained, "for Salt Lake Knit. And I've never seen a girl who would look better in a soft knit dress than you would, Julia."

"Nolan!" Margie hit him playfully.

"Salt Lake City, and you work out here in Chicago? Isn't that awfully far from home?" Julia asked.

"It's my territory. Temporary assignment. I love it. New hunting ground, right, Margie?"

Margie smiled and shook her head. "He's incorrigible. Oh, didn't you say Elmwood, Julia? This is it."

The car lunged and cut a wide arch, but it made the corner. It wasn't far to Julia's apartment. Nolan pulled up in front of the building, and before Julia could open her door, he was out and over to her side to help her. His hand felt lean and strong against her arm. She waved a last farewell to Margie and walked up the path with Nolan.

At the steps he paused and pulled out a pen and notepad from some inner pocket.

"Let's see . . . Julia Wilde." He wrote with a flourish as he spoke. "Freeport, Illinois — a hundred miles west." He paused and considered her with a wry smile. "Give me your address if you dare, Julia, and I'll stop by one of these days and sell you a knit dress." He paused and brushed back her loose brown locks playfully. "A perfect deal for the girl with the perfect figure."

Julia felt herself color under his gaze. To cover her confusion, she took the pad and wrote her street address, then handed it back. Nolan's fingers closed gently around her hand, resting there a moment before he drew them away.

"I'll be seeing you then, some sunny day in Freeport." He turned and walked off.

"I'll look for you," Julia promised.

Nolan paused and glanced back at her one last time, intently. "Now don't you go getting lost again, Julia Wilde. Though I can't say I'm sorry you got off at the wrong stop tonight."

Julia watched him get into the car and drive away. *What a strange adventure! I wonder . . . will I ever really see him again.* She stepped into the welcome warmth of the apartment, still seeing the laughing eyes and hearing the cocky, but kindly young voice.

*   *   *   *   *   *

The train from Chicago ran through some beautiful country. Miles of rich Illinois fields stretched newly planted, or with the black earth turned in readiness for the seed. Julia could lower the window and smell the earth and see the farm wives calling to hens or children. She loved it here, the land and the easy ways, the peaceful sense of everything right with the world.

It was hard to imagine this spring of 1943 that somewhere there was war. Somewhere cities were burning and people in pain, and children hungry, crying through the streets. Her own life was so much in order that it frightened her. Too good to be true. Perhaps too good to last . . .

She buried the thought; she wouldn't allow it to spread. She was going home from two weeks successful training. Marc would be there waiting. Marc and her family, and a new position, and summer around the corner. And she was young, and in Freeport there was no war.

At the station she spied Marc before the train stopped moving. He really was a handsome man to look at. Thick black hair and eyes of a summer sky blue. The prince straight out of the storybooks of her childhood. She hurried to reach the aisle and the door and his arms.

He gathered her up and held her against him firmly. She could feel his heart beat and smell his mellow cologne. When he kissed her, it seemed new, like the first time all over again, and it left her trembling.

"Perhaps you ought to go away more often," he breathed against her hair. "I hadn't expected . . ."

He left the sentence hanging. She brushed his cheek with one last, gentle kiss, glad to know he was feeling the same way she did.

"Where's Mother?" she asked. "And Laura?"

The station platform was beginning to empty now of people and boxes and bags.

"They said if I brought you home in time for supper, I could have you to myself for the afternoon."

"I won't object to that."

"I hoped you wouldn't."

He took her hand and led her to where the car was parked in a shady, secluded spot. He kissed her again, a long, possessive kiss, marveling as he did so often, how this woman—so warm, so charming, so vitally lovely and loving—had come to be his.

"Just think," he said, releasing her with a smile, "you can bend my ear all afternoon, and then get to tell everything over again to your family tonight."

"You know me too well, Marc," she laughed.

"Not as well as I plan to." He drew her to him again with a sudden, intense hunger and kissed her, although people were walking nearby.

What was happening? Julia wondered. *Why this sudden, serious vein?*

"We'd better get going." Julia helped herself into the car. Marc drove off, down the quiet, familiar streets.

She was content to sit back and enjoy whatever Marc chose for them. They had dated each other since high school. Now, three years later, he was perhaps the most important part of her life. They fit one another—knew each other's moods and tastes and opinions. In another year Marc's education would be complete, and then . . .

The car turned in the broad, tree-lined entrance to Krape Park. Julia smiled to herself. The perfect spot to come. If thoughts of the war and what one more year might bring teased nastily at her mind, she refused to notice. Tucked away in the park like a gentle, meandering monster wound the broad, quiet river, lined with trees and ferns and dusty old caves. And in less than ten minutes Marc would push off a canoe and they would be part of the quiet and the peace.

An hour later found them still on the river's surface. Julia trailed her hand through the cool, clear water, shaking the sparkling drops from her fingertips. Marc cupped water into his hands and splashed her playfully.

"I don't know about you; you're becoming quite the woman of the world. A little professional down to your fingertips. A few years ago Bata didn't have women managers."

Julia wondered if any real resentment lay behind the mild teasing. "Opportunity for women. What's wrong with that?"

Marc wrinkled his face in a frown that was almost a scowl. "Nothing, I suppose. I'm just wondering who I'll get to take care of my children and cook my meals and . . ."

"Hush! You're a wretched tease!" She splashed him in turn, and the canoe rocked gently in protest. "Well, I intend to play as much as I work this summer," she declared.

Marc smiled. "That's one resolve I'll be glad to cooperate with." He folded his arms and leaned back, regarding her gently.

"Just think, Marc, we've the whole long summer before us."

"Yes, and it might be the last. It might well be all we have."

His words made Julia start. Though spoken so casually, they seemed to bring with them a chill that she instantly felt.

"What do you mean, Marc?" she asked, not certain she wanted the answer.

"My deferment expires in September," he said. His voice was so soft she had to strain to hear it. "I doubt very much I can land another. Uncle Sam's caught up with me at last."

"But what about school? What about your grandma? And Louise?" What she meant more than all was, *what about us?* But she didn't say it.

Marc was the sole support of his aging grandmother. His

parents had died when he was only twelve. His retarded sister, Louise, was also considered Marc's legal dependent. The terrible war that sucked up so many men had somehow found room to consider Marc as an individual—a luxury, Julia knew, but she'd come to depend upon it.

"It's worked for awhile," Marc replied, his voice nearly expressionless. "They're legitimate enough. But at length the war takes precedence over all."

She did reply. There was nothing she could say right now that she wanted him to hear. She reached for his hand and held it between her own. Too perfect to last.

The air seemed suddenly chilly, the river dark and secretive and withdrawn.

*Are you a god? would you
create me new?*
   SHAKESPEARE

———————————————————————————2

It was June now, and the Illinois heat was coming into its own. *Stifling,* Nolan thought, *this heavy, sticky humidity with no mountain breezes at night to cool things off.*

He washed down the last bite of his hamburger with a swig of cold 7-Up. Oh well, it had been a good spring for him. He shouldn't complain. Chicago, Joliet, Rockford—he'd set up large accounts in every one. Nothing out here could compare with his line of goods. And no stodgy Midwestern salesman had mastered the techniques that came quite easily to a returned Mormon missionary. He smiled to himself. Of course, he did have charm. But charm, by itself, doesn't get a guy very far. He prided himself on other qualities, too. Good organization, a natural business sense, and a willingness to work and keep on working. That's why he had landed this job with an extra gas ration, and the rare opportunity in war time to travel this way.

He took out his little black book and marked off his completed schedule. That would do it here in Rockford for a week or two. It was back to Chicago and Margie and nights on the town with other young Mormons whose company he enjoyed. If Nolan knew how to work, he knew even better how to enjoy himself.

He thumbed through the notebook and something caught

his eye; an address penned in a careful feminine hand—1136 Lincoln Drive— and the name above, in his own writing—Julia Wilde. An instant image rose up before his eyes. He tapped the book on the counter top thoughtfully. Should he go? Now was the perfect time. He was in between, with a few free days to spare. Freeport was only forty-five minutes from here. From a business standpoint, one good sale would pay for the trip. He might even set up accounts that would keep him coming. From a personal standpoint? He remembered the long shapely legs, the soft lips, the deep, intelligent eyes. What would she say when she saw him? What fun it would be. A challenge. Nolan could never resist a challenge.

He checked the clock above the greasy counter. He could be in Freeport by mid-afternoon. Surprise her where she worked. What was the store? Bata — Bata Shoes, that was it. He chuckled out loud. His mind was already teeming with half a dozen new-formed possibilities. He paid for his meal and hurried out to his car, aware that he cut a pleasing figure in his cream suit and open-necked shirt. Forty-five minutes to Freeport, and what then? Nolan could barely wait to find out.

*   *   *   *   *   *

"I'll bet you sell more nylons here than shoes. That is, if you can convince the ladies that their legs will look like yours when they put them on."

Julia turned sharply, an angry retort on her lips. But it died when she saw the grin on the harmless face. "Nolan!"

He cocked his head. "I told you I'd come, didn't I?"

"Some sunny day in Freeport," Julia quoted. *He came!* she thought, her pulse racing. *He really came!*

"And here I am," Nolan smiled. "As good as my word."

"It's quarter to five," Julia stammered nervously, checking

her watch. "Do you think you can sit over there for fifteen minutes and stay out of mischief until I can close this place?"

With exaggerated gestures Nolan complied. Julia, going about her tasks, could feel his eyes following her. He was as charming, as crazy as she remembered him. And in broad daylight his blond good looks were quite arresting. She sighed a little. Oh well. At least he had timed his appearance well. It was Thursday today. And Marc spent every Thursday night with his grandma. At least she wouldn't have explanations to make. After Nolan had come and gone she could casually mention it. That is, if he was cooperative about leaving.

They ate that evening at *The Downs*—country-cooked chicken and ribs. An excellent place that catered to a slightly older crowd. There wouldn't be many of Julia's friends there on a week night.

Nolan proved to be a delightful companion, thoughtful as well as clever and entertaining. Julia was curious when he didn't order coffee.

"You don't look like a 7-Up man to me."

He grinned. "I take it that's meant as a compliment?" He twirled his glass and assumed a mock innocent air. "How do you suppose I keep these fresh, boyish looks? Clean living, young lady. It works every time." The tone of the words was more serious than she expected. Then suddenly everything clicked.

"Utah . . . Salt Lake Knit. Of course, you're a Mormon!"

"Spoken like a true Gentile—with just the proper tinge of abhorrence and horror."

"Oh, Nolan, I didn't mean . . ."

He laughed at her now. "No, no, I shouldn't have teased you. It's all right. I'm used to being a curiosity."

"Well, what is a Mormon, anyway?" Julia asked. "All I know is . . ."

"Please, spare me all you know!" He raised his fine eyebrows in a line of mock distress. "You know, in all the years I've been explaining it, I've never come up with the pat, five-minute answer. Which is really all that anybody wants."

She detected something behind the light tone of his words, but she couldn't read what it was. Then their food arrived, and the conversation dissolved into other things. Neither tried to revive it through the night.

In the hushed, lovely evening Julia showed him the city: the streets of fine mansions, the charming old courthouse, and the site of the famous Lincoln-Douglas debates. He was sincerely interested, asking clever or intelligent questions in turn. When they drove through the park, he couldn't hold back his delight.

"This is the next best thing to the mountains I've ever seen."

They stopped and walked the path by the waterfall. But Julia felt vaguely uneasy. The harsh word "betrayal" came into her mind, and she couldn't brush it away. This spot belonged to Marc. For that matter, everything she had shown him tonight was part of their own very special and personal world. She had no business allowing a stranger to intrude. Yet, what choice did she have? She couldn't sulk like a child, refuse to be even polite.

This is harmless, anyway, she told herself. But she knew the throbbing in her veins was far from harmless, the way she felt walking close to this man on the narrow path. Once he took her arm to help her over a rough spot. She thought for a moment that he might kiss her. The deep, dancing eyes had held hers like a spell. But it passed. Perhaps he had sensed that she wasn't ready, that an intimacy would do him more harm than good.

What he really thought was, *Nolan, don't be so foolish. You fall in now, and you'll never get out again.* He had never been so moved by a woman's beauty. So he dropped her arm and allowed her to walk ahead. Nolan liked to play the role of the trapper, not the part of the trapped. A woman with too much power made him uneasy. And this one, he knew, could play havoc with his life. That is, if he let her. He had never yet made that mistake; of letting a powerful woman get too close. He had no intention of making it now. So he watched her graceful movements as she walked, thanking his lucky stars that little Freeport was totally out of the beaten path for him.

He meant to leave the next morning. Julia had decided on the pale pink knit suit she wanted the evening before. There was nothing to really keep him. But, when the morning came, he had trouble getting away. The day was too lovely; there was something restless inside him.

The bulletin board at the hotel where he was staying had a poster advertising a weekend dance. He showed up mid-morning at Julia's shop, trying to appear as casual as he could, feeling too close to nervous for comfort.

"Hey, what kind of band does this fellow Jack Russell sport?"

Julia studied him. "He's good," she said quietly. "Not Benny Goodman, by any means, but he's good."

"You wouldn't be interested in . . ." He caught the look on her face. "You already have a date."

His expression looked almost comical in amazement, curiosity, mock hurt—all the emotions he could play with and manipulate at will. Julia pushed back her hair.

"Well, yes . . . well, kind of. Not really."

The mock emotions dissolved. "Then there *is* a boyfriend. I should have known as much." He paused only slightly. "Well, I'll be off . . ."

Why did she feel *sorry* for him? Drawn, as to a little boy

15

who'd been hurt?

"Listen, Nolan, I don't think it will hurt, I mean, well. . . if you'd like to stay . . ." Why couldn't she find a way to say it?

He was studying her, and she was unable to read his look. "My dear, I'm not the type to court trouble. Besides, I left my dueling pistols back in Utah."

Julia laughed, in open relief as well as amusement.

"On the other hand," Nolan continued, wearing again one of his assumed expressions, "it might do this fellow good. Rattle him a little. Shake his security. Make him take a second look at what he's got."

"Agreed. Now why don't you get lost for a couple of hours? I've got to get *some* work done today. I'll see you. . ."

"For lunch," he interrupted. "How's 1:15?" His blue eyes sparkled.

She nodded, shaking her head in hopeless defeat. With a flourish he was gone. Julia stood watching until he was no longer in sight. It was all very fun, very clever. But hers was still the task of talking to Marc and finding some way to explain.

*   *   *   *   *   *

As it turned out, Marc's reaction surprised her somewhat. He displayed very little curiosity. She explained about meeting Nolan in Chicago, never expecting him to really show up; but here he was, and she had to do something with him. Marc agreed. He didn't storm angrily, nor retreat into a hurt silence. Baffled was the word. He acted a little baffled, but that was all. Julia hung up from the conversation with an almost flat taste in her mouth. Usually it was easy for her to tell what Marc was thinking. She didn't like this too-casual barrier which Marc's response seemed to have created between them.

16

But the evening with Nolan was a total success. He was clever and entertaining, yet thoughtful as well. She enjoyed the furtive looks both friends and acquaintances gave her. She enjoyed introducing him to people, and appreciated his sincere, interested responses. His attentions were flattering. She had to admit that it was exciting to be out with a handsome, charming stranger and to have everyone see and know it. And Nolan was an excellent dancer. She could have been content to spend the entire evening in his arms. She liked the way he held her and touched her. She liked the hint of mischief in his smile. She liked the open admiration she could read in his eyes.

Julia's younger sister, Laura, was also at the dance with her boyfriend, Ross. Laura had been extremely curious about the blond-haired stranger. Early in the evening she and Ross appeared at their table, each sporting two beers and laughing and joking good-naturedly. Julia glanced sidewise at Nolan, wondering what he would do, berating herself for not remembering to say something to Laura about Nolan being a non-drinker. She shouldn't have worried. Nolan bantered back and forth with the young couple for awhile, then casually shoved his beer over to Ross, grinned, and said, "Drink mine for me, will you, buddy?"

"Gladly," Ross replied, taking a long swallow and smacking his lips. "I see you've already discovered how to impress Julia."

Nolan shrugged his shoulders, and they both laughed. It was true; Julia disapproved of too much drinking, and Ross seemed always to be a little over the edge. So it had worked out very simply after all.

The evening had ended much too quickly. Nolan drove home slowly through the warm, dark shadows, and they talked of pleasant little things. At the door Julia invited him in, but he shook his head.

"No, I've imposed on you enough as it is."

She began to protest, but he touched her lips with a gentle finger.

"Really, Julia, thanks for putting up with me. I've never had a more real and wonderful time in my life."

He leaned forward and brushed her lips with his own; a sweet, beguiling little kiss which sent a shiver through her. He drew away but continued to gaze at her, his blue eyes penetrating deep into hers.

"Might I show up again sometime? Would that disturb you too much, Julia?"

He seemed too serious; Julia felt uncomfortable without the tease, the sparkle there.

"Please do," she said, feeling frustrated, wishing she could come up with a clever reply. "And give my best to Margie, will you?"

He nodded, touched her hand, smiled an almost melancholy smile, and was gone. Julia watched him saunter easily down the walk, wave once, climb into his car, and drive away. She opened the door and walked into the house, and realized she still was trembling a little.

Nolan didn't sleep very well that night. He had bent and then broken his own cardinal rule: never get involved with a pretty girl, never let a woman gain power over you. His dreams were of Julia, sweet and garbled, and he awoke feeling worn and drained, not rested.

As he headed out of town and back to the highway, he knew the smartest thing he could do was to never come back again. He had met a pretty girl, made a good sale, had an enjoyable weekend. Let it go at that.

At the last minute he stopped by a corner drugstore with an outside phone booth. He flipped through the pages, found the number and street address, and without too much difficulty located the dingy but clean little apartment. He rang and then rattled the door, but there was no answer. Well, the boys were out working like they ought to be.

He found a piece of paper in his car and scribbled a note, at the bottom of which he carefully printed Julia's name and address. Then he stuck it inside the elders' mailbox. They ought to find it easily when they came home from tracting. He got back into his car and drove away. Whatever else he did or didn't do, he felt better now.

He reached the highway and let the car wind out into a gentle, purring speed. He flipped on the car radio, knowing he couldn't face the long drive with the company of his own thoughts. The sun shimmered in waves along the heated highway, but the air from the open window lifted Nolan's hair and cooled his skin. Freeport fell behind, and there was nothing but sun and road and the next curve ahead.

*　*　*　*　*　*

For a few days following Nolan's surprise visit, Julia had to fight a feeling of deflation. She found herself turning at the sound of a strange male voice, or starting at each opening of the shop door, experiencing a strange sense of disappointment when Nolan failed to materialize before her eyes. Things crawled at a mellow summer pace, anyway, but Julia didn't like the lethargic, almost drugged feeling inside her own head.

Marc didn't help. His attitude remained amazingly casual and disinterested. He seemed to take the whole situation at face value only. The stranger had shown up, Julia had graciously altered her own plans and entertained him. That meant a little inconvenience to Marc and perhaps a little pleasure to Julia. But it was simple, and it was over with, and he hadn't even questioned her for details. It wasn't as if she wanted to really hurt Marc or that she'd have known what to say if he had decided to ask. *What was it, then?* she asked herself over and over. The experience had been more real than she wanted to admit, and it was difficult for her to shrug it off and forget it.

Yet in every other way things went well, and Julia felt very happy with her life. She tried to savor each day with Marc, fearful of his gloomy prediction that spring day on the river. Nolan became more of a memory as everyday living pushed him out of her thoughts.

The first weekend in July, Julia's parents took the train to Peoria to spend some days with her mother's sister and her husband who lived there. Julia's father worked for the Illinois Central, and it was their habit to take advantage of the free fare and go visiting at least one weekend out of each month—more during the summer months and nice weather. Julia and Laura were older now. It was easier to leave them home on their own together.

Julia had enjoyed a lovely Saturday and a long evening with Marc and slept late on Sunday morning, refusing to feel guilty that she had missed attending church. She washed her hair, took a leisurely bath, and ate a light luncheon with Laura. Shortly after two o'clock the doorbell rang.

Julia opened the door to find two young men standing on the porch, wide warm grins on their faces, both wearing dark suits, white shirts, and ties. Her confusion must have shown in her face.

"We don't mean to disturb you, miss, but we were wondering, well . . ."

The first one started off fine but then seemed to hesitate. His friend continued for him.

"We're looking for Julia Wilde."

"I'm Julia Wilde," Julia replied, her tone not altogether

inviting.

"Could we come in, Miss Wilde, for just a few moments and visit with you? We're Mormon missionaries, and we've been working in this area . . ."

Julia didn't realize how fierce her expression had become.

"I don't believe it. Nolan sent you. He did, didn't he? How could he do such a thing?"

The two young men looked bewildered, then embarrassed. They shifted from foot to foot. One took out a white handkerchief and wiped his forehead.

"I don't know exactly what you mean, Miss Wilde, and we certainly don't wish to offend you. If you'd rather not talk with us, we understand. We certainly . . ."

Julia was beginning to feel badly. They were so sincere and so uncomfortable.

"No, I'm sorry. Excuse me, I've been very rude. Please come in."

She held the door open wide and urged them with a bright smile. She had a few moments to wonder how Nolan had sent them and why. It didn't seem like the kind of thing Nolan would do. The two of them hadn't even talked of religion.

When the two young missionaries were seated, Julia sat opposite them, determined to be calm and gracious no matter what.

"Now, how did you find me, gentlemen? I mean, you knew my name. You came here on purpose. You just didn't happen to knock on my door."

"Well, Miss Wilde, we do sometimes work on what is called a referral system. Members having friends who have expressed an interest in the Church—or whom they think might be interested in the Church—give their names to the missionaries, and we . . . we contact them . . . to see if we might be of some help." The missionary with the glasses had a very charming, boyish smile.

"But that wasn't quite the situation with you," the other young man confided. "Your case is a little bit . . . unique, you might say."

Julia couldn't help returning their smiles. She was tempted to say, "That is because my case involves Nolan Hart. Anything involving Nolan is bound to be out of the ordinary." But she merely smiled and held her peace.

"You see," the freckle-faced missionary continued, "we came home one afternoon from tracting and found a note stuck in our mailbox. It gave your name and address and said. . ."

He hesitated and glanced toward his companion. His companion nodded encouragingly.

"I don't think it would hurt to tell her what the note said, Elder Blair."

Elder Blair coughed quietly and then continued. "The note said, 'This young lady would prove a delightful addition to the flock in this area. Tract her out if you feel like a challenge—and don't let her beautiful tabernacle deceive you. She has a spirit every bit as beguiling and superb.'" Elder Blair coughed again and looked down at his feet.

Julia felt her cheeks going hot, then a sudden, more compulsive feeling. And to the astonishment of the two uneasy young men, she laughed out loud.

"Oh, that's Nolan, all right. Nolan to the letter." She could almost see the expression on his face as he wrote it, tucked it in the mailbox with a little pat, and walked back to his car, pleased with himself, his eyes sparkling.

So the three of them laughed together. And after that it was easy to talk. Julia listened. She asked a few questions. The missionaries spoke fluently, telling her the Joseph Smith story, explaining the basic doctrines of priesthood, revelation, and a personal God. It was almost too much for Julia to grasp. There were things that startled and amazed her; almost repulsed her. Yet there was a fascination as well, something which drew her interest and attention, almost against her will.

Before they rose to leave, Elder Turley offered a prayer. It was different from any prayer Julia had ever heard. She could feel the young man's sense of ease, as well as his sincerity and love. It was as though he were speaking to someone he was familiar with, someone he understood and trusted. As he spoke, a warm feeling came over her; delicious and peaceful it seemed to flow through her entire body. After the prayer was over the feeling lingered. She took the tracts the young men offered; she thanked them and was surprised at the warmth and sincerity of her own words.

"You read those over and think them over and give us a call when you feel you're ready for another talk."

The smile on the freckled face was gentle and understanding, and Julia felt glad she had confided to them her fears concerning her family. Her mother was one of the most zealous Baptists she knew, and her father just as committed in his quiet way. It made her shudder to think what they would do if they could see her now—entertaining two young Mormon missionaries in their own home, listening to doctrines they would consider wicked and extreme.

A slight shudder of guilt ran through her. She closed the door on the two smiling faces and felt suddenly frightened and alone. What was she doing listening to them? There was no place in her life for this kind of a religion. She wanted no part of turmoil and discord. She was happy with what she had and what she was.

She walked into the kitchen and was about to stuff the tracts into the garbage sack beneath her mother's sink. But she hesitated. What if her mother were to notice them there? What else could she do? Burn them? Tear them into little shreds? She laughed out loud, a nervous little laugh. *I'll just tuck them in one of my drawers for now,* she thought. *I can always decide what to do about them later.*

She climbed the stairs to her room and placed the papers carefully far back in her bottom drawer, beneath layers of folded sweaters. Once they were out of sight, out of her hand, she felt better. She was glad Laura had gone off with Ross before her strange visitors made their appearance. No one need ever know they had been here. *But could she forget? Could she ignore the things they had told her?* She buried the question, refusing to give it an answer, refusing to heed the new thoughts that would trouble her.

The telephone in the hall jangled loud in the silence. Julia started and ran to lift up the receiver. Never had she been more relieved to hear Marc's voice!

"Yes, yes, come over and get me right away. I'm going stir-crazy alone in this quiet house."

She touched up her lipstick and rouge and brushed her hair, loving the feel of it soft against her shoulders. It would take Marc at least ten minutes to get to her house. She flew down the stairs and outdoors into the sunlight and waited on the steps till she saw Marc's car. Then she ran to him and touched his lips in greeting, pleased to read the welcome in his eyes. She was determined to drive out the last of the shadows that teased and whispered so cruelly at the edges of her mind.

3

Well, what remedy? . . . What cannot
be eschew'd must be embraced;
Then must thou needs find out new heaven,
new earth . . .
SHAKESPEARE

Several days passed before Julia remembered the tracts. She retrieved them and stuffed them into her zippered purse, determined to throw them away when she got to the store. But when she sat down at noon with a sandwich and salad, the tracts were still in her purse, so she pulled them out.

The titles, bold and tantalizing, seemed to leap at her: *The True Nature of God, The Joseph Smith Story, The Law of Tithing, Which Church Is True?* Which church is true? That ugly, glaring question. She stared a moment longer, then opened the offensive missive and, in self-defense, began to read.

She was ten minutes late to work when at last she glanced at the clock. Reluctantly she closed the pages and placed the materials back into her purse. All afternoon her mind was teeming. That night in her room she read the rest of the tracts, then re-read part of the one that told about God. It was late when she went to bed, but she couldn't sleep. Too many questions and new ideas churned through her head.

This was a Tuesday. On Thursday afternoon she called the number the missionaries had left her. Both Laura and her parents would be gone that night. She asked Elder Turley to come and to bring more tracts. This was a bear on her back—a face that leered in the darkness. It was her own fault to have let the thing begin. But now she knew that she had to see it through. With a curse beneath her breath for the fair-haired Nolan she closed up the shop, angrily pushing away the feelings of betrayal which came whenever she began to think of what she was about to do.

Elders Blair and Turley stayed for two solid hours, and they came again on Sunday afternoon. Julia read every tract they had to give her. On Sunday they handed her a small, leather-bound book.

"Read this," Elder Blair said softly, "but not without praying. You must pray as you read, or else you'll be wasting your time."

The book felt cool and smooth against her fingers. She wanted to tell them she didn't know how to pray. But the words stuck in her throat, so she smiled a little and took the paper Elder Turley held out.

"Moroni 10:4 and 5. Read that first," he told her.

She thanked them both. She knew they wouldn't push her. But she knew she needed to follow this through to its end.

The next day, Monday, Marc came to take her to lunch. It was breathlessly hot—the still, choking heat of late July. Julia sipped a cold lemonade and toyed with her food.

"You've become quite the mysterious woman, Julia," Marc said, and raised a dark eyebrow, regarding her quizzically. Julia felt her stomach turn and her muscles quiver.

"What do you mean?" She hoped her voice sounded casual—light and casual. She stirred the ice in her drink and sipped through her straw, keeping her eyes downcast as she heard his reply.

"What do I mean? Good heavens, Julia. First a tall, blond stranger walks suddenly into your life. Oh, yes, you duly protest, but you do enjoy it."

She glanced up briefly, trying to guess at his mood. Just a

hint of hostility, mostly a teasing banter.

"He's no sooner gone than appear two other strangers. Nice, proper young men whom you entertain in your parlor. But only when Mama and Papa are gone away. Very quietly. And you mention their visits to no one."

"All right. All right." Julia swallowed the lump in her throat. "You don't have to be sarcastic, for heavens sake." She glared at him, in wounded self-defense. "Surely you must know . . ."

"All I know is this. You've shared everything with me for the past three years. Now, suddenly . . ."

"Oh, Marc. It's not like you think."

"Yes, it is, Julia. Don't try to kid yourself."

She looked at him then and could see the pain in his eyes. Pain and confusion.

"Come on," she said, "let's talk."

He paid the bill and followed her out to the street. The heat rose from the scorching pavement and clung about them.

"You need to get back to work. This'll keep," he said. His voice sounded quiet, a little tight and restrained.

"I'm never late. Louise can carry on for awhile. We need to talk now." Her voice was trembling a little.

They drove to the park. He pulled up where the ground was shaded, where tall trees closed off the sun and the outside world. He shut off the engine and all about them was silence. He quietly sat watching her, waiting for her to speak.

"It's innocent enough, Marc. It's just . . . well, complicated."

Julia felt like a small child, explaining some naughty offense. She didn't like the feeling. She started again.

"It's simple, Marc, and has nothing to do with romance. It's much more simple and dull than that. Nolan, you see, happens to be a Mormon."

She paused ever so slightly, but Marc didn't seem to react.

"I didn't know that at first," she continued. "In fact, we never talked about it. But he gave my name to the missionaries here."

"The two young men in suits who appear on Sundays?" Marc's voice sounded more normal and relaxed.

"That's right. They came one day, and I let them in."

"That makes sense. You were surprised, maybe curious. And, of course, you would do the polite thing." Marc smiled, and his smile seemed kind. "But why more than once? And why did you keep it from me?"

"I'm not sure. I'm not sure, Marc." Julia pushed back her heavy hair.

"Are you really interested?" He looked at her hard now.

"I don't know! I . . ." She returned his gaze, somewhat helplessly.

"Come on, now, Julia. It has to be this Nolan."

Julia had never heard his name on Marc's lips before. It gave her a start.

"You're more drawn to him than you want to admit," he continued. "Why else would you bother with all this religion stuff?"

"That's not true," Julia cried. "And why is it so impossible to be interested in religion?"

"Well, Julia, you never have been. Why suddenly now?" His voice was low, gentle, but also probing.

"Because it came up now! It hit me square in the face."

"And if Nolan wasn't in the picture, what would you have done?"

What was the matter with Marc, bringing up questions like that? "I don't know. I haven't thought through that kind of thing."

Marc didn't reply, but the silence seemed louder than

words. Finally Julia spoke, measuring each word carefully.

"I may have let the missionaries in the first time because of Nolan—because of that connection. But after that I was interested, Marc, honestly. I read what they gave me. I had questions I wanted answered."

Marc shook his head and ran restless fingers through his hair.

"I won't pretend I understand that, Julia. You don't seriously want to get involved with these people, do you?"

She had no real answer. "I haven't thought it through that far," she told him honestly.

"Well, you'd better," he warned, and his voice sounded hard again. "Come on, I'd best get you back."

He turned on the engine. Julia watched him, struck with how handsome his features were—fine, chiseled lines, skin rich and smooth and golden. He turned back to her, a gentle smile on his lips.

"Mormonism. That's not for you," he said. "You want to go out to Utah and be one of Nolan's polygamous wives? I don't think you could handle that very well."

He was teasing her, but kindly. He drew her close. When he kissed her, it was lingering, hard, and possessive.

"You belong right here with me, Julia. Don't you forget it."

The words, which should have given her comfort, were strangely disturbing. As if he were deciding something for her. But he was only expressing the way both of them felt! Then what were these other feelings that rose unbidden, swirling lines of confusion through her mind? She looked at Marc and knew that she really loved him. Then why this sense of searching, this discontent?

That night she brought out the book the elders had left for

her. She leafed through its pages and found at the very end the scripture Elder Turley had told her to read:

> "And when ye shall receive these things, I would exhort you that ye would ask God, the Eternal Father, in the name of Christ, if these things are not true; and if ye shall ask with a sincere heart, with real intent, having faith in Christ, he will manifest the truth of it unto you, by the power of the Holy Ghost.
> And by the power of the Holy Ghost ye may know the truth of all things."

Julia knelt down beside her bed. She felt awkward and strange. She closed her eyes, but it was harder to close her mind, to clear it of crowding thoughts and outside sensations. At last she said a few words, but not out loud. Simple words, spoken uncertainly. She rose to her feet feeling better, feeling relieved. Settling down on the bed, she opened *The Book of Mormon* and began to read the account which Nephi had written.

She read that first night twice as long as she had intended. Tuesday evening she read and prayed again. It was easier the second time. She liked it better. A tiny seed of confidence started to grow.

Wednesday evening Nolan called long distance. She heard his voice with a sinking in her stomach.

"Have the missionaries come to bother you yet?" Did his voice, for the first time she knew, sound a little uncertain?

"Yes," Julia told him. "That wasn't quite fair, you know."

The laugh that followed was Nolan, with no reservation. "I thought you were spunky enough to turn them away if you wanted."

There was a little silence before he continued, more serious now. "I'm sorry, Julia, if the whole thing's upset you. I'm not even sure why I did it. I just felt, well . . ."

He hesitated, and Julia held her breath.

"I just felt you were too special not to, I guess."

She didn't quite understand that, but he wasn't stopping to explain.

"You may not be interested, then, in what I was going to ask you," Nolan was continuing, the uncertainty back in his voice.

"I'm ready for anything," Julia replied, and that brought back his laughter.

"I'll be in Rockford through the weekend, and I thought I might buzz over on Sunday and get you. Let you see what a bunch of Mormons is really like."

"That might be a good idea. I'm sure you're far from a normal example."

"C'mon. I bring out the worst in you," Nolan protested.

Julia laughed. *Why not?* She was curious. No. She was interested. Sooner or later it would come to this, so why not now? Get it out of her system. Find out once and for all.

"All right, Nolan. I'd like that. But how about just picking me up at the Greyhound station in Rockford?"

"That's not necessary."

"Oh, yes, it is," she assured him.

He believed her and let it go. They arranged a time. She hung up the receiver and stared at the now silent phone. Her parents would be gone again, so any danger there was done away with. But what about Marc? Could she just not tell him—again? After the talk they'd had on Monday, she'd have to tell him. She dreaded the idea. Oh, why should it be like this? She was simply showing interest in a religion. Marc cared little for religion of any kind. Why should he care what she did with that part of her life?

His words came suddenly, startlingly to mind. "Come on

now, Julia, it has to be this Nolan." She didn't think it was just Nolan. Nolan was fun and delightful—and flattering. But she was in love with Marc. Then what was it, really? What drew her toward something that brought her such problems and distress?

She would have to find out. And Sunday ought to help, ought to make a difference. But what kind of a difference Julia refused to let herself consider.

Julia spent Friday night and all of Saturday with Marc. At first she had thought to tell him right away, get it off her chest as casually as she could. But in the end, uncertain of his reaction, not wanting to spoil the weekend, she put it off. As it happened, Marc led into the subject himself.

"Are your young, dark-suited friends coming over tomorrow?"

Julia smiled as she answered, as charmingly as she could. "As a matter of fact, I have an adventure planned for tomorrow."

"Oh?" The dark brow creased, though the voice was still casual.

"I'm taking the bus to Rockford—to go to a Mormon meeting."

Marc's laugh was harsh and short. "You have to be kidding. What in the world's gotten into you, anyway?"

Julia kept her tone, her expression light and indifferent. "I've been reading a lot. Now I want to see for myself."

He glared at her but didn't reply.

"I'm following this thing through, Marc, so you might say the sooner, the better."

"I never expected something like this from you," he muttered.

"Oh, Marc!" She hugged his arm and touched him lightly.

"Please don't be so morose. I don't mean to upset you. It's nothing that has to hurt us in any way."

He looked at her, reticent still, unbending.

"I won't argue, Julia. But we'll see what we shall see."

His words made her shudder, in spite of the close, warm night. But they dropped the subject and, after a few moments, forgot—or pretended to— and the evening wore on. The close feeling between them was back, and Julia pleased him in every way she could to make up for this thing, this barrier between them which she had created. When he kissed her, the sweetness sent shivers running through her. She wished he would offer to go to Rockford tomorrow; show some kind of interest, at least some support. She had thought they were so thoroughly part of each other. But in this new desire she stood alone.

When Marc took her home, she went straight up to her room. But she didn't read, and she knew she couldn't pray. There was too much she wasn't willing to face right now. She got ready for bed as quickly as she could, determined to wait and see what tomorrow would bring.

Marc dropped her off, then turned around the corner and pulled his car up against the curb. He could see the lighted square of Julia's window, the delicate lace of the curtains that fringed the sides. He sat there a moment, just thinking about the girl who had become the very reason for his living. He was more afraid than he wanted to admit. He could see, much more than Julia, how she was changing. A thought came, hard and unyielding, into his mind, a thought he had never suffered before. *Was there a chance—a real, live chance—he was losing Julia?*

The wedge of bedroom window turned dark and dissolved. Marc pulled away from the curb and drove slowly home, feeling suddenly old and very tired.

Nolan was waiting when Julia arrived at the station. The morning was clear and lovely, cooler than most. As he drove, Nolan kept up an easy flow of conversation. Julia's mind was teeming with questions, but she held them back. She was more nervous than she had thought she would be. Nolan pulled up outside the Odd Fellows Hall, a beautiful old brick structure in the heart of the city.

"Well, this is it. A fitting place, actually."

"The Odd Fellows Hall— what do you mean, a fitting place?"

"Mormons are an odd people, Julia—face it. A peculiar people, the scriptures say."

"The scriptures would mean in a good way. Do you mean that, too?"

Nolan's face was very serious as he answered, with a warmth in his eyes Julia hadn't seen there before.

"In many good ways the Mormons are peculiar." He held her eyes, and she felt something tingle inside. "I wouldn't have drug you into this, believe me, if I didn't feel in my heart I was offering you the best."

Julia nodded and swallowed a nervous lump in her throat. Nolan winked and patted her hand.

"Come on, pretty lady, let's go."

Once inside Julia was surprised at the number of people. And all of them seemed to come and say hello! More than superficially polite, they seemed warmly, sincerely interested in her. And the children! There seemed to be children everywhere.

When they took their seats, there was organ music playing, but it wasn't a tune that Julia recognized. Everything in the service was different for her. Yet nothing seemed really alien or strange. The two-and-a-half minute speakers from the audience interested Julia, and she was impressed by the young people who handled that assignment so well, wondering at her own ability to stand up in front of an audience that way.

One of the speakers talked about the pioneers and the trek to Utah, and the practice song was "Come, Come Ye Saints." Julia loved it and after awhile could sing along. The last verse especially moved her.

> We'll find the place which God for us prepared,
> Far away in the West,
> Where none shall come to hurt or make afraid;
> There the Saints will be blessed.
> We'll make the air with music ring,
> Shout praises to our God and King;
> Above the rest these words we'll tell—
> All is well! All is well!

There was a dignity woven into the enthusiasm she felt here. Not the stuffy pompousness some churches displayed, but a deeper sense of respect toward Deity. And again that impression of naturalness she had felt with the elders, as though these people knew and felt comfortable with their God. It was evident in their discourse, their songs, and their prayers.

Following the service, which Nolan explained was only Sunday School, a kindly, middle-aged couple came up and asked if she and Nolan would come to their home for Sunday dinner before sacrament meeting. That was a term Julia had never heard before.

The couple, Brother and Sister Landbourn, made Julia feel at home. The food was delicious, the atmosphere kind and relaxed. There were two of the Landbourne's children still living at home. A pretty teenage girl and a boy named Johnny, who followed Nolan about like a little puppy.

The hours passed quickly and soon it was time for the second meeting. Nolan contrived to get Julia aside and asked, with concern, if she wanted the whole treatment in one day. She assured him that she could endure one more meeting.

"You're just looking for an excuse to sluff," she teased him.

At sacrament meeting Brother Landbourne was one of the speakers. He spoke beautifully about the restoration of the gospel, the importance of having God's authority restored to earth, the beauty and power of the Prophet Joseph Smith's life. Julia couldn't help wondering if his message had not been chosen on her behalf, but she felt no preachiness in his presentation, no finger shaking at her, no negative pressure.

A young mother, leaving three children behind on the bench, then rose and sang a solo in a lovely, clear soprano voice. The second speaker, a younger man, spoke on brotherly love.

The idea of no paid ministry astounded Julia. She could see before her eyes how well it worked, even in what they told her was a small, poorly staffed branch. It brought religion down to a personal level; everyone having a right, as well as a duty to understand, everyone sharing the privilege and growth of participation.

Again, at the meeting's close, she was greeted by many and thanked for coming. She was warmed by the touch of their hands and the touch of their spirits. Elder Blair and Elder Turley smiled from a distance. Julia wondered what they would have to say the next time they met.

Nolan insisted on driving her home. He didn't question her much about the day but listened to her impressions and answered her questions. There was none of the sharp-edged humor about him now. Julia felt secure and relaxed in his presence and very much at peace.

At her door she invited him in, but he shook his head.

"You've had enough of us Mormons for one day," he insisted. "Listen, Julia, is it all right to call you again?"

"For Sundays or other times?" she asked quietly.

He regarded her for a moment and cocked his head. "For both, if that's not pushing things."

Julia took a deep breath. "It might be just now."

He nodded instantly, and she felt that he understood without feeling rejected.

"Could you please keep it just on Sundays for awhile? I've so much to sort out . . . and so many people to . . ."

She paused, not able to think of a word she wanted. People to juggle, to please, to placate somehow.

"I understand. I . . ." Nolan paused, then went swiftly on. "It will be worth it in the end, Julia. Please believe that."

He touched her hand, very gently, before he left her.

That evening Julia read *The Book of Mormon* until her head nodded and her eyes began to burn. Then she dropped to her knees and for the first time really prayed. Something was happening deep within her heart. She no longer felt afraid nor wished to ignore it. The seed was a good seed, and Julia was letting it grow.

Marc asked her about the day only casually, so she answered him just as casually in return. It was interesting, she said, and she wasn't quite certain what she thought yet. He scowled but made no attempt to criticize. Though that, in itself, was a barrier between them. There was a part of Julia now that she could not share with Marc, a part that grew stronger, more tangible every day.

Near the end of the week she called her family together. Sunday was approaching, and Julia intended to return to the branch in Rockford again. Her parents would not be away over the weekend. Now was the time; she could put it off no longer.

She started at the beginning, haltingly. After the first few words, her mother began to rave. But her father insisted they hear out Julia's story, and she was left to continue before a curtain of silent, staring faces.

"Oh, Julia, Julia, how could you?" her sister kept saying.

"I don't understand! I just don't understand." Her mother's voice was harsh and unrelenting. "How could you come to like a boy who's a Mormon? What have we done to deserve this, Julia? This terrible mockery of everything we've taught you."

"I'm not interested in Mormonism because of Nolan." Julia struggled very hard to maintain her patience. "And it's not as though you've been teaching me all my life that being a Baptist is the only way."

"Julia!" Her father's voice was soft but carried a note of authority.

"Oh, Daddy," she appealed. "You know what I mean. You and Mother have only been active Baptists a few years yourselves."

She thought fleetingly of the ways her mother had bended—allowing Laura to date a Lutheran boy, allowing the girls to attend the local dances. But this, of course, was altogether different.

"That doesn't matter, Julia," her father was saying. "We don't wish to force our way upon you. There are other ways we could come to accept."

"But Mormonism! Why, it's not even a Christian religion!" Julia could taste the disdain in her mother's tone.

"Mother, this isn't the dark ages. All the stories you've heard. . ."

"Stories!" Her mother was pacing, angry, self-righteous now. "Gold plates and angels and mobs and polygamy!" Her voice rose higher with every hateful word. "Don't tell me that isn't true, my girl, don't tell me! How could you think to get mixed up with such perverts, such fiends?"

Julia bit her lip and sighed. What could she reply? Her mother's kind of prejudice wasn't open to reason.

"I'm sorry, Mother. I'm sorry it had to happen. But now that it has . . ." She spread her hands helplessly.

Her father walked over and gave her a little squeeze.

"Let's sleep on this, Amelia," he said to his wife. "Emotions are too high. We've talked enough for one night."

Julia felt tears gather behind her eyes. Her parents were hurt and confused. And could she blame them? And yet, she couldn't deny what had happened to her; the things she had come to know—the things she felt.

She climbed the stairs to her room and closed the door. And when Laura knocked very softly, she didn't answer. She couldn't face her sister's incredulous, innocent blame.

Yet, surprisingly, once alone, a peace came upon her. She dropped to her knees and prayed, and the feeling grew. She knew she had to do what she felt was right. She thought of Moroni's words. She thought of Joseph. He had lived so near, right here in her own Illinois. People always thought of "those Utah Mormons," but here the gospel had unfolded and grown. It was here that the Prophet bore the load on his shoulders and sealed his testimony with his own blood.

Her own trials were so much less than those of the Prophet. And yet, she understood she was not alone. Just as Joseph had never been alone. This personal God she was coming to believe in was mindful of her in a real and loving way. He would give her strength, He would guide her if she let Him. The beauty of that kind of knowledge coursed through her soul.

She could do what she had to do for what she believed. She

could walk, though falteringly, the path that others had broken.

*'Tis not strange that even our loves
should with our fortunes change.*
SHAKESPEARE

4

A nd so the wheel of change began to turn. Julia felt it, but she could not view its progress, nor guess how new and different she would be when the change had taken its full toll. And change snatched time and routine from her hands, cheating her and shortening her pleasure.

August came, more sultry than July, days where the temperatures rose above one hundred, and the humidity was nearly as high. The days slowed, and people sought the shade. And in their lovely park, now choked and crowded, Marc told Julia that their summer was over.

"I have to go," he said for the second time. "It's a chance to make a little extra money. And you know I need all the money I can get." There was no bitterness in his tone, only resignation.

"Well, don't pretend you won't enjoy it." Julia hated to hear her voice sounding petulant.

"Of course, I'll enjoy the work, the playing. Do you want me to be thoroughly miserable?"

"No, no!" She kissed him lightly on the cheek. "You may be called . . . you may not need the money." Why couldn't she just say the thing outright?

"You mean I may go to work for Uncle Sam instead? That's right. And I'll know, come September."

She studied his face to see what his feelings were. But Marc was working hard at concealing them.

"If that happens, the money's yours. You can blow it all on your trousseau."

Julia forced herself to smile and join in his banter. Anything to cover up the pain, the chasm that was growing between them.

Julia watched him as he rowed with long, easy strokes. Everything Marc chose to do, he did well. He had a natural ear for music and had been playing the piano since he was five. Piano and guitar were merely hobbies for him. But a boy in his cousin's band had broken his arm, and Andy needed an extra, needed it badly. Who else but Marc? And Marc did need the money. And Champaign, Illinois wasn't far away. Why did she have such a sinking in her stomach?

She trailed her fingers aimlessly through the water. Scant weeks ago she had sat in this very canoe, newly back from Chicago, flushed with life, totally secure in her own powers to make her world do what she wished it to. But even then the wheel had already begun to turn. She hadn't seen it or felt it, but ever so slightly the movement, the change, had chewed at the threads of her life.

Marc left, without much fanfare or ado. A longer, hungry kiss in the silken darkness, a promise to write, a gentle word or two. Then he was gone, and the days were dull without him. Julia worked and read and waited for the weekends, the Sundays in Rockford that now were her meaning in life. She increased her sessions with the elders, too. She learned and grew and changed as the wheel kept turning.

Late in August, Nolan came to Freeport. He took Julia to *Angelos*—the most exclusive restaurant in town. And there, over dinner, Julia told him she wanted to be baptized.

"Well, I'm glad I happened to choose some place fitting to celebrate." Nolan couldn't quite keep the surprise in his voice from showing. He leaned across and took her hand in his.

"Are you certain, Julia? I mean, it's no light decision."

She nodded, meeting his gaze with her own.

"It will change you forever; it's a whole different way of life."

"I've learned that," she said, her voice very quiet, yet strong.

He kissed her fingers but did not release her hand. "I'm happier than you know." He sat silent a moment. Then suddenly tapped his plate with stacatto fingers.

"What is it?" she asked.

He looked up expectantly. "Have you told your folks yet?" The fingers kept softly drumming.

Julia shook her head. She thought of the many sessions with her parents, her mother's ranting and raving and tears. They wouldn't stop her, but they were no more reconciled than they had been the first evening she told them.

"No, I haven't," she answered Nolan, "there's time for that."

He nodded as if to say all right, you know best. But the thoughtful look was still in his eyes.

"What of the other man in your life?" he asked, contriving an expression of concern half-serious, half-mockery that nearly set Julia laughing.

"Marc's opposed to everything about this, Nolan."

"And that's made things pretty rough between you two?"

"No . . . not exactly." Julia struggled to express something she wasn't certain about herself. "He hasn't been pushy, just silently unaccepting—a little withdrawn."

Nolan shifted in his chair impatiently.

"I don't understand this guy. I'm sorry, Julia. You two

aren't exactly high school sweethearts anymore. If he's so crazy about you, then after all this time why hasn't he . . ."

He paused in mid-sentence, realizing how far he had gone.

"Why hasn't he asked me to marry him?" Julia smiled slightly. "He has, in his way, a dozen times or more."

Nolan raised his eyebrows and waited expectantly.

"Marc was born," Julia continued, "on the other side of the tracks. His father was poor, his parents uneducated. But his father's sister married the richest doctor in Freeport."

Nolan whistled under his breath. "The plot thickens."

"She was ashamed of her brother and didn't have much to do with him. When Marc was twelve, both his parents were killed in an accident. He and his one sister—a severely retarded girl—went to live with his widowed grandma."

Nolan fidgeted a bit, uncomfortably. "What about the rich aunt?"

"At first she had little to do with them. But then she started to take a liking to Marc. She hasn't been exactly the kindly, motherly type . . ." Julia winced just thinking of Marc's implacable aunt. "But she did do one thing for him. She built a desire, an obsession almost to obtain an education. She convinced him he could do something with his life."

"Well, didn't she help him financially as well?"

Nolan sounded affronted, and Julia had to smile.

"At first she did. But everything she gave him was so tied up with strings, so . . . condescending. At last he rejected the help and just took the advice."

Nolan nodded, his warm, open features covered with sympathy.

"The war . . . well, the war made worse an impossible situation. Marc's determined to have something to offer me."

"But he has!" Nolan began to protest.

Julia held up a hand to stop him.

44

"His faith in himself doesn't go that far," she explained, with a sad little smile. "He needs something tangible to offer. He's terrified that he may still end up like his father."

"I can understand that." Nolan's voice was very gentle. "What complicated creatures we humans are!" He made a little face, more pathetic than funny. "And I suppose your becoming a business woman yourself hasn't helped."

"That's right. And now one more show of independence—one more way I don't need him in my life."

"I should never have written that note to the elders."

Nolan made the words sound like a statement of fact. Julia couldn't discern what he felt when he spoke them.

"That's right," she agreed. "I've thought that a thousand times. You've turned my life topsy-turvy, and you know it."

"I had no idea . . ." His voice and his eyes were sincere.

"What's done is done, and you know you don't really regret it." She gazed across at him and softly quoted his own words. "I wouldn't have drug you into this, believe me, if I didn't feel in my heart I was offering you the best."

Nolan stared at her, without reply. *What a girl, what a girl!* he thought. But he didn't say it.

"It's mine now," Julia continued. "You offered it, and I accepted. Now there's only one way to go from here."

Nolan smiled and stroked the hand he still was holding. "There's a district conference in Bloomington on Sunday," he said. "We'll try to make the arrangements there."

Julia smiled softly. "My birthday's the end of September, and it falls on a Sunday. Do you think we could do it then?"

"I can't think of anything more perfect," Nolan agreed.

In Bloomington, after the second session, Nolan arranged for Julia to meet with the mission president. President Mack was a stout, bristly person with bushy red eyebrows which framed two of the keenest blue eyes Julia had ever seen. A man in his middle fifties, he seemed at ease with the authority he carried.

After pleasantries he asked a few general questions and listened to Julia's answers carefully. Then he directed the gaze of his blue eyes upon her.

"We don't rush into baptisms in this Church," he said. The words were no-nonsense, but the tone at least was kindly.

"Tell me." He paused, and his eyes seemed to pierce through hers. "Is it this young man you're interested in, or is it the Church?"

The question was difficult for Julia. She continued to meet his gaze and answered calmly.

"I'm interested in Nolan, but if I never see him again, I still want to be a member of the Church."

He nodded and grunted and seemed, at least, satisfied. But he repeated his earlier words in the same level way.

"Well, young lady, we don't rush into baptisms, you know."

They talked a little longer and, in spite of his sternness, Julia found herself liking and trusting the man. When she rose to leave, he put his arm around her and gave her a quick, fatherly squeeze.

"Thank you for coming, young lady. It's been delightful. I'll see you again."

Those words were the only encouragement she had.

When she reported the interview to Nolan, he shrugged his shoulders.

"Can't second-guess James Mack, that's one thing I've learned. We'll just carry on till we hear what the man's decided."

Julia nodded. That was fine with her. She had a sense of

some kind of pattern working, weaving with a beauty and symmetry of its own. She wouldn't disturb the tracery of the colors, for fear of spoiling something she would not know how to repair.

*   *   *   *   *   *

Marc returned in the middle of the next week. Julia prepared a special candlelight dinner and listened to his tales of the past few weeks, taking pleasure in his voice, his face, his nearness.

After a while he leaned back, well-fed and happy. His gaze as he looked on Julia was warm and inviting, so his words seemed out of place and were instantly jarring.

"Well, what have you been doing to keep yourself busy? Your letters didn't say much to give you away."

Julia ignored the barb and smiled back at him.

"The same old routine but empty without you here."

"You mean your Mormon didn't pop in to fill my place?"

"As a matter of fact, Nolan was here last Friday night." Julia saw Marc's swift reaction, in spite of his efforts at control.

"For the first time since you've been gone," she continued primly. "And I haven't been to the park even once."

She paused and touched his cheek ever so slightly. "I would never want to go there without you."

He seemed impervious to her charms, to her honest emotions.

"But of course, you went to Rockford every Sunday."

"I told you I was going to. That's not news."

"And?" The word came out cold and demanding.

"And?" She had no idea what he wanted.

"And where do you stand now—in reference to all this nonsense?"

Julia took a deep breath. What a miserable way to start. This would be worse than she had even anticipated.

"You don't need to be so biting and sarcastic."

"Is that right?" The misery flickered across his face. "Would you rather I didn't care at all?"

With a sinking feeling Julia realized that he had no other choice but anger and opposition. If only he could accept such an innocent thing as a change in religion—live compatibly with this part of her. But a voice inside her own head instantly chided her. *This isn't a mere change in your religion. It's a change in your thoughts, in your heart, in your way of life.*

He was watching her now, impatient and expectant.

"Well, I've had time—as you know—to study and consider. The more I've learned, the more it's made sense to me."

She hesitated, hating to say the words. "The more I've grown to love it, Marc."

He didn't move. No flicker of eye or body betrayed his mind.

"I've decided to be baptized, Marc."

She watched him closely. For a moment there was no movement, no change.

"Did I come back too late or just in the nick of time?"

The words were spoken more to himself than to her. He fumbled in his pocket and drew out a paper. Silently he handed it to Julia.

Her fingers trembled as she unfolded the creases. It was his official notice of induction. Less than two weeks from now he would be gone. The time had slipped through their fingers. The end was here.

"I'm asking you to marry me, Julia. Now, before I go in. Will you be my wife?"

He didn't move a muscle, nor change his expression.

Not now . . . not like this! Julia cried inside. *Not hard and*

48

cold and hurting!

"You're not asking me to marry you," she told him. She didn't know what she said till she heard her own words. "You're giving me a cold ultimatum—you or the Church. This has nothing to do with love—or wanting me to share my life with you."

She was drained now, and her voice was nearly a sob. "This has nothing to do with what we were together!"

The last word rang in the silence like some cruel echo. Together . . . together . . .

"Marc, look at me!"

Julia knelt beside his chair, so her eyes were level with his, so he couldn't ignore her.

"Do you love me, Marc? Tell me! Tell me you love me!"

She forced back her tears and watched him, silently praying to herself. The muscles of his face twitched once or twice, and his eyes were pools of pain she could hardly bear. But his voice, when he spoke, was controlled and carefully empty.

"You had no right to make that decision without me, Julia. Not if you love me—not if we're part of each other."

She winced with the pain his words bore into her.

"Yes, it's me or Mormonism. You have ten days. I'll be waiting to hear your answer."

He somehow got out of the chair without touching her. She sat back on her heels and watched him leave, helpless to stop him, helpless to ease him in any way. He was what he was, as much as she longed to change him. And Mormonism had no place in his life. The blackness of the truth rose up before her: Mormonism had become her very life!

Sunday she went to Rockford as usual. It was three days since Marc's return and, true to his word, he hadn't called. He was waiting for her—and she already knew her answer.

Nolan ran to meet her, his face like a shining candle.

"You won't believe this. You'd better sit down," he said.

He seated her with flagrant ceremony, his eyes bubbling over with what he had to say.

"Yesterday the mission home called me. The president wished to see me. 'Could you please stop in,' his secretary asked, 'any time today?'"

"You were there in fifteen minutes." Julia couldn't help smiling.

Nolan laughed with her. "How well you've come to know me."

"Well, go on," she urged, and he grinned, enjoying her attentive anticipation.

"When I got there, I was ushered right in to the president's office, madly wondering which of my sins had caught up with me at last." He grinned. "But it wasn't me he was interested in."

Julia felt a slight flutter in her stomach. Something must have shown as well in her face.

"That's right," Nolan continued, "the topic was you. 'Is that pretty little gal still interested in being baptized?' he asked me."

"Did you tell him, 'Yes?'" Julia's eyes were round as saucers.

"Well, I thought I ought to tell him the truth. 'She's cooled down a little,' I said, 'these past few weeks.'"

"Nolan!"

"All right. No more teasing. I'm sorry, honey." He took both her hands and repeated the president's words.

"Sometimes the convert isn't worth the cost of renting the baptismal font. But in this case I think your young lady will be. Tell her she can be baptized on her birthday."

Julia squealed as Nolan twirled her once around. She hugged his neck, her eyes moist and shining.

"What made him change his mind?"

"I'll never know. But you, my girl, are a dry-land Mormon no longer."

Less than two weeks till her birthday! There was so much to do. And, of course, at the top of the list was the one thing she dreaded, the one thing that could cast a shadow on this day: she must talk to Marc and give him her decision.

Marc must have known before she spoke a word. He backed away and didn't attempt to touch her, hiding his own pain with guarded eyes.

"I don't want to marry you now, like this," she argued. "It would be starting out with everything wrong between us. It wouldn't work that way."

"It wouldn't work anyway now. You've changed. You aren't the person you were before."

His voice refused to betray emotion, just like his face. Julia wondered if he was thinking *before . . . before when I loved you.* She wanted to ask him what he felt for her now. She knew she had changed, she couldn't argue that. She wondered if Marc had also changed. Why didn't he fight for her? Why must it be like this—backing her into a corner and making her choose, with no warmth from him, no love to help her along?

"I'll be baptized, and you complete your training. Then we can see . . ."

He moved with an angry gesture. "You'll be deeper in your direction and I in mine." He shook his head and looked at her with sad eyes.

"I hope you know what you're doing, Julia," he said.

Something within her froze at his words.

"Will you write to me, Marc? Will you . . ."

She paused and swallowed. She wanted to say, *will you please keep loving me?*

"I'll write. And I'll be back after basic training."

"I'll be here."

She tried to smile, but her face seemed frozen. She wanted to take him into her arms, she wanted to hold him!

He nodded, his own features twisted painfully.

"Good-bye, Julia."

He held the door for her and watched her leave.

"Good-bye, my love," he whispered under his breath. Why had he failed to keep her? What weakness pushed him toward his own destruction? What pride choked back the pain that was in his heart?

You taught me how to know
the face of right.
SHAKESPEARE

————————————————————————5

J ulia walked through the next few days in a fog, numbed by her pain so that nothing seemed to touch her. And though Marc left and the day of her baptism grew nearer, the sense of unreality didn't recede.

On Tuesday evening she met with the elders and asked them to pray for her. To her surprise and relief, she felt their prayer breaking up some leaden darkness inside her. That night she prayed—for herself, for her family, for Marc. And as she prayed for him, a peaceful feeling overcame her. When she rose again, she knew she would be all right. She felt the sense of purpose and guidance again.

She had long since decided to keep her baptism secret. Her mother's hatred and venom would spoil everything, she knew. The pain for her parents would be no less before or after. Perhaps once it was done her father would at least respect it. At least they would know how fruitless their opposition would be. And she would have the experience of her baptism to cherish, to tuck away for strength when she needed it.

It seemed Time's wheel had skipped a clog or two and jerked too quickly forward. There was no time to grasp the constant changes. Marc, herself, her baptism—and now Nolan.

He had already, by wit and charm, arranged an extension

from his company just so he would be here for Julia's baptism. In less than a week he, too, would be gone from her life. Not much would be left but her own new self and convictions and a world in which nothing was easy, familiar, or known.

*   *   *   *   *   *

On Sunday morning Julia celebrated her birthday with her family, postponing her trip to Rockford till afternoon. She would go to sacrament meeting, then her baptism.

The day was exquisite, an Indian-summer day. The elm in front of her house, brilliant with color, was only one bright spot in a sea of autumn trees.

Like the autumn her past was dying, too, serene and peaceful, transformed with a cry of beauty—all that was old within her dying away—reborn new and pure and endless with promise.

She was twenty-two years old today. And today marked the beginning of a new life, a new inner self. Her past was behind her now, and all the beginnings her future held still shrouded from view.

Julia was the only person being baptized. Sister Landbourne helped her dress and explained the procedure. There was such a warmth and sweetness in her nature; no mother could have been more tender and concerned.

When she walked down into the water, Elder Turley was waiting. His hand, when he took hers, felt firm and warm. So brief the words, so wonderful the feeling that trembled through her, strong and sure and true.

When she rose up out of the water, her eyes found Nolan's, and they seemed to mirror the joy that surged through her heart.

Dressed, with her hair brushed out, at least partially dry, she entered the little room where her friends were waiting—brothers and sisters in every real sense of the word who hugged her and kissed her and understood perfectly the importance of what she experienced this day.

They sang "The Spirit of God Like a Fire," and Julia couldn't keep the tears from her eyes. As she felt the hands of the priesthood on her head, a current of power, a testimony, surged through her soul, and she knew without doubt that what she was doing was right.

The peace, the warm glowing inside, remained to sustain her. When she arrived home, drained and tired, her features still shone. Laura looked up from the magazine she was reading.

"What's happened, Julia?"

"What do you mean, what's happened?"

"You seem different." Laura closed the magazine and looked closer. "What have you done? I fixed your hair when you left. Look at it now, hanging straight on your shoulders."

Julia walked over and took her sister's hand.

"I was baptized tonight," she said softly.

"You mean . . . baptized a Mormon?"

Julia nodded.

"How could you—how did you ever find the nerve? Why didn't you tell us before? What will Mother do?"

"That's why. I didn't want to spoil the day. Now Mother can scream and rave all she wants. But today was perfect, and nothing can ever touch that."

Watching Julia, Laura felt a strange discomfort—as if she was in the presence of someone she didn't know, someone peaceful and secure and apart from her. Julia was so quiet, so utterly feminine. She had never dreamed her sister would have the strength to go her own way against so much opposition.

Julia bent and kissed her cheek, and her lips were cool.

"Please don't mention it, honey. Let me tell Mother myself."

Laura nodded and watched her sister climb the stairs, so graceful, so self-contained, so *happy.* It was easy to feel how happy Julia was. Laura sat, the discarded magazine in her lap, and wondered what could possibly change a person in the amazing way she had watched her sister change.

"I'd have locked you in your room if I'd have known. I would never, never have allowed this thing to happen!"

Her mother's lips were a tight thin line, her face white and drained, but her blue eyes smouldered. Julia trembled, watching her helpless rage. But reminded of the fear behind the anger, she impulsively threw her arms about her mother and held her close before she could protest.

"I love you, Mother," she said, her own voice choking. "Please try to forgive me for hurting you this way."

Her mother drew back, but her features had softened and broken. She mumbled something and hurried out of the room.

Julia felt, in days after, that her long, patient prayers had been answered. There were no more confrontations, no brutal words. Her mother kept her feelings to herself—something she rarely disciplined herself to do. There were still times she could feel her mother's tension, see the anger and pain on her face. But the accusations never again were spoken, the bitterness retreated into silence.

Grateful, Julia worked to make up the difference and showered her mother with kindnesses and love, anxious to begin the healing process.

Nolan came the day before his leaving, clever and charming even in his good-bye.

56

"I'm back to the desert." And he added, with a wink, "God's country."

Julia smiled indulgently.

"I'll miss you," he said.

"Nonsense, with all those fresh-faced mountain girls."

Nolan grinned. "Well, they say Utah grows the prettiest girls—even if it can't grow anything else. But I don't expect to find many who can measure up to you."

Julia chose to ignore the compliment, even though a warmth was creeping into his tone.

"What about all the girls you left behind?"

Nolan cocked his head back thoughtfully. "There's one or two I'm anxious to check up on . . ."

"Nolan, Nolan!" Julia shook her head. "Margie was right—you're hopeless, incorrigible."

He took her hand. "Well, it was a lucky day for me when you got lost."

The warmth was strong in his voice now and in his eyes.

"Julia, listen," he said, "I've been thinking—seriously. Will you hear me out?"

She nodded. *Good heavens, what now?* she thought. *With Nolan, you could never guess.*

"I'm worried about you alone here," he began. "Marc's gone, I'll be gone . . ."

"As if life couldn't go on without you two," she protested, feeling a little annoyed at him suddenly.

"That's not what I'm trying to say. Let me start again." He ran a restless hand through his thick blond hair.

"You're the only Mormon in Freeport, Julia. You know that. It's not easy now, and it's bound to get even harder. Getting to Rockford every week, with the ration on gas—you won't even have someone close to talk to, you know."

Julia realized how sincere Nolan was. It touched her, and

she waited for what would come next.

"I think . . . well, I wish you'd consider coming out West."

"To Utah?" Julia breathed, and her heart gave a jump.

"That's right. You ought to be with the Saints," he said.

She shook her head. "My parents would never accept that—my going over a thousand miles from home!"

Nolan leaned closer, his voice more persuasive and urgent.

"It's your life, Julia. Just look what you've done so far. The worst has already happened with your baptism."

Her eyes grew wide as his words ran through her head.

"How can you grow in the gospel alone, this way? Meet other Mormons, come to find yourself? It won't work here. Can you see that? Can you, Julia?"

She gazed at him, not answering either way.

"I know it's overwhelming to think about. But do that—think about it. It's your future, Julia. You've got to do what you know will be right for you."

Something in his words rang a note within her, and excitement—or fear—seemed to course through her veins.

"There aren't any Mormon men here," he said, with no sparkle in his voice to lighten his words.

"So you want me to come to Utah to find a husband?"

He spread out his hands as if to say, "And why not?"

"The happy hunting ground," he assured her. Now the sparkle was coming. "Fair maid, I am pleased to tell you, there are many more at home like me."

Julia laughed out loud.

"I'm right," he said. "That's where your future lies. Not here—not any longer."

"Well, I'm glad you're so sure."

There was a little note of resentment in her voice.

"Pray about it, Julia. See what happens. I think you'll come to know what you have to do. Will you?"

He held her eyes; he wanted commitment.

"All right."

She sighed. He put his arm around her and drew her close.

"Poor Julia. How many times have you cursed that night in Chicago?"

"You mean cursed that arrogant young man who walked into my life and proceeded to take it to pieces before my eyes?"

He winced. "Do you ever regret it? Do you, Julia?"

"If you mean the Church, no, not for a minute," she answered.

His face bent closer; she knew he was going to kiss her. She felt his lips press gently against her own. Something within her rose up in a fierce response, and the kiss became a burning, living thing. It had never been like this with Nolan before.

Julia drew back, trembling, but Nolan stared at her, then pulled her to him again. Struggling, protesting, this time she pushed him away.

"It's a good thing this never happened before," she breathed. "To think what I've been missing all this time!"

He was shaken enough that he didn't care how it showed. He was lucky to be leaving, that he knew. Otherwise, his doom might lurk in those liquid eyes, in the lips and spirit and mind of this lovely girl.

Julia didn't attempt to unravel her feelings but steered Nolan back to safer, calmer waters. When he left, the ease was there once more, the open comaraderie they'd known.

"I'll write," he promised, "and do all I can to entice you."

"And when I arrive, you'll add me to your list—one date every other month as my name comes up."

"I've made a regular cynic of you, Julia. You'll find someone better than me, I've no doubt of that."

Julia felt suddenly tired, just thinking about it. Man-hunting appeared a gruesome game to her. It seemed she had always had Marc since she could remember, and then the spice of Nolan was added as well. And now nothing remained but a lonely and dull sort of aching.

He didn't kiss her again before he left. But he drew her close and held her tenderly.

"Sweet Julia, please be happy," he whispered. "Take care of yourself until I see you again."

So he left her, after all, with a taste of sweetness, and a resolve in her heart to try to be happy. Though just what happiness was she didn't know. Somewhere deep inside she had the feeling that happiness for her was a nameless face, a tomorrow totally different from today—a dream she hadn't even begun to dream.

*   *   *   *   *   *

Autumn that year took a long time dying. As though the world, inundated with death, deserved a few last days of flaming splendor, one last cry that beauty had been there, before the final breath of surrender, and all that was dark and cold and drab moved in.

Julia worked during the week and went to Church on Sunday. She did a lot of reading, a lot of walking through the peaceful city, and a lot of thinking she never had done before.

Until now, the war had seemed so remote. Suddenly she was aware of the newspaper headlines, the citizen efforts at sacrifice and support—people donating thousands of volunteer hours, donating their blood, buying fat war bonds, growing victory gardens, collecting trash (scrap metal, rags, old newspapers), anything to have a part in a war that was now their own. It struck her strongly how much she had lived to herself, in a world of unreality and dream, supposing the war would ignore her and pass her by, allowing her to live in a time that no longer existed.

Suddenly she was aware of the propoganda, the songs that blared on the radio day and night, most of them jarring offensively at her ears: "You're a Sap, Mister Jap" and "We're Gonna Find a Feller Who Is Yeller and Beat Him Red, White and Blue" and Sammy Kaye's "Remember Pearl Harbor March." Trash, as far as Julia was concerned. But then, the strains of "You Made Me Love You" and "Don't Sit Under the Apple Tree With Anyone Else But Me" would assail her, touching small points of pain somewhere inside.

Why could they make her cry as if heartbroken? What was she crying for? What did she mourn? What was she losing? What did she even want?

Marc had become what they called "a ninety-day wonder." After three months of intensive training and indoctrination, he returned to Freeport, two weeks before Christmas. He was ready now to go off and die for his country. This was the last, the final, the real good-bye.

He had changed more physically than she had expected. His body looked lean and hardened, his thick hair whacked short. There was something hard and remote in his face, the soft, boyish glow brushed off and gone forever.

He didn't want to talk much about himself. Julia couldn't help wondering what harsh realities he had met with to prepare him for something worse than reality—the nightmare men call war and glory and winning. She couldn't read what had happened inside of him, and she knew he would never share that with her again.

At first it was hard to talk to each other at all. He seemed surprised when she told him Nolan had gone. They talked about her parents, her sister, his grandma. They relaxed a lot, but the old warmth wasn't there. Whatever they had been existed no more. Each of them knew it, but neither knew what to do about it.

She had to insist before he'd agree to write to her, though she knew from his eyes he had wanted to all along. He asked her to keep an eye on his sister and grandma, and she gave him her word, intending to keep the promise as long as she could.

"You'll write to me then, as soon as you get resettled?"

He was rising to leave, and though she wanted to keep him, if just for a few minutes longer, Julia knew there was nothing to hold him for anymore. He nodded and brought out a gift and handed it to her.

"Don't open it till Christmas," he said with a grin that nearly broke her heart.

She wanted to tell him she loved him, because she did. Even if it wasn't the old love she gave him before, even if it was only the ashes of what had been, she loved him, and she wanted him to leave at least with that love.

At the very last moment he turned, for he couldn't help it, although he knew he was torturing himself. He looked at her hard, as though memorizing each feature, then slowly drew her closer and closer against him.

When he kissed her, wet tears were already on her face. He kissed her eyes, her cheek, her silken hair. He found her mouth, and they clung to one another, hungry and hurting, giving in one desperate kiss the last of a love that refused to burn out and die. All the tenderness of the past, all the pain of the present fused them together with a fire of passion and longing.

Breathless, Julia pressed her head on his shoulder, and he stroked her hair as he used to. And there, against the ache of his beating heart, she poured out her grief and love, and he could hear her, but she wasn't forced to watch the pain in his eyes.

When he left her, she thought her tears were all cried out.

But nothing could stop the flow from her burdened heart. Far into the night she wept and whispered his name, and wrestled with dreams and memories sweet and bitter, till at last the tears began to purify, and sleep came like a healing balm. The blanket of darkness covered all suffering and longing and hid for awhile the scars that were etched in her soul.

*　　*　　*　　*　　*　　*

The spirit of Christmas fell like a blessing on Julia's family, soothing some of the soreness, purging the grief, renewing the spirit of love they had shared before. Marc's first letter came and a note from Nolan with a postcard picture of the winter temple shrouded in snow. Julia and Laura went to see Bing Crosby's "White Christmas" and shed tears in the darkened theatre more than once. The radio and newspaper journalists wanted to make it a "Pearl Harbor Christmas," playing and replaying the events of the year before, feeding the fire of patriotism to feverish pitch.

Julia worked hard at shutting the war from her mind and enjoying this bright holiday with her family. Whenever she could, she spent the time with her mother, and the two of them baked every Christmas concoction they could afford.

One grey afternoon, while a soft snow swept at the windows and the fragrance of new-baked gingerbread filled the room, Julia sat at the kitchen table sipping hot chocolate and visiting with her mother while the gingerbread cooled. A question that long had bothered her came to her mind, and she felt impressed to ask her mother about it.

"Mother, before you met Daddy, before you were married, were there any other men in your life?"

Her mother looked up and smiled in a slow, soft way.

"Other men or another man?" she asked.

"Well, another man, actually," Julia admitted.

"You want to know if I was ever in love before."

Julia nodded and watched her mother's expressive face.

"Good heavens, I haven't thought about it for such a long time, Julia."

She got up and refilled her cup with steaming coffee, then sat and regarded her daughter thoughtfully.

"There was one man in my life before your father." The words came slowly as old memories began to stir. "I was just seventeen, and he was a good deal older. I met him at the library where I worked."

"The one that's still there? The big old Bloomington library?"

Julia's mother had been raised in Indiana, and the family had visited her home town several times.

"That's right," she continued. "He was a college student and had come to work on a research paper."

Julia smiled. "Did you get to know him well?"

"Oh, yes, very well."

Her mother's voice had altered, and Julia looked up, more sharply interested now.

"What kind of a person was he?" Julia prodded.

"Intensely attractive, intensely interesting, and intensely sure of himself. Always sure of himself, no matter what."

"Good heavens, Mother. Well, what was he like—with you?"

Her mother paused a moment. "It's hard to explain that. He wasn't the gentle, flattering kind of man. But he was thoughtful and attentive, and when you were with him, you always felt as though you were someone important."

Julia nodded. "And?"

"And—remember how young I was. I fell very hard, and at first I was more than willing to be his little shadow, his other

64

self."

"What do you mean?"

"Well, a woman to him was much like an alter-ego, a sounding board for what went on inside himself. Once he had honored a woman with his attentions, with making her part of him, that's just what he expected—total emergence in what he was and did."

"That's scary."

"Yes, it was frightening after awhile. I realized how little he knew of *me*, how little he cared for what I wanted in life."

She shook her head, and a slight smile curled her lips. "He was almost offended that I should think of myself—that anything should come before his wishes."

"Whew! Well, he doesn't sound very lovable to me."

"Oh, but he was, in his own enigmatic way. So full of boyish fun and enthusiasm. Eager to please to a point. And, you see, his life was colorful and interesting. So 'going along with him' could prove very exciting. And besides," she paused briefly, "he was very, very rich."

"Oh."

Julia sipped her chocolate and waited. As her mother continued, a shadow crept over her face.

"I ignored what I saw as long as I could ignore it, hoping against hope that something would change. Face it—both he and his money were very attractive. I kept telling myself they were worth the price I would pay."

"Did he ever ask you . . . well, did you really come close to marriage?"

"Oh, yes." The shadow grew in the grey-blue eyes. "He gave me a ring—one huge glittering diamond surrounded by rubies. We talked about dates, we even talked about where to live."

She leaned back in her chair and smiled at her daughter,

and Julia read many things in her eyes that she left unsaid.

"I would have married him, I'm sure of it. I could never have broken away on my own. But, as things turned out, I didn't have to. You see, I met your father first."

"You did?"

"Yes, and so I had someone else to turn to. And I could see what it was to be loved, as well as to love. Your father . . . well, I bloomed under his attentions. I realized how subjugated I had become. I'd suppressed so much of me for so long. It was like finding myself again, coming back to life."

"How did you ever tell him? What did you do?" Julia felt a shudder, a sympathetic response pass through her.

"It was the hardest thing I've ever done in my life. I told him it wouldn't work with us—and I told him why. Very direct, and as kindly as I could. But I never told him there was another man."

"Why not?"

"I knew I was hurting his pride already. It didn't seem necessary to hurt him any more."

She stirred her cooling coffee thoughtfully. "Besides, I think I feared him just a little. Who knows what he might have done if he'd known about Douglas?"

"Did you ever see him again after that?" Julia was thoroughly enchanted by this heretofore undiscovered part of her mother's life.

"No. Our paths would not have normally crossed, anyway. It was shortly after this that I moved here to Freeport and lived with my aunt until I married your father."

Julia nodded, remembering well those early stories.

"He never even tried to see you then?"

"To win me back, you mean?" She shook her head.

"And he took back the gorgeous diamond?"

Her mother smiled. "Yes, of course, with the dire

prediction that I would always be sorry. Regret what I had done till the day I died."

Julia shivered a little. "Have you, Mother? I mean, have you ever regretted it, even a little bit?"

Her mother paused before answering, and Julia waited, wanting to know the answer for many reasons, fears, and feelings of her own that still would not give her peace.

"No, honey, I can honestly say that I never did. Oh, there were times I thought about him—wondered what he was doing and where he was. There were even rough times when I thought about his money—more wistfully, I'll admit, than I thought of him!"

They laughed a little at that, then her mother continued.

"But I always felt at peace with my own decision—that I'd done what was right, even though it was hard."

She paused. Julia, watching, could see that the next words cost her some inner struggle.

"Sometimes in life you have to stand on your own and do what you feel is right, no matter what."

Julia felt a mist rising in her eyes. She reached across and took her mother's hand. There was nothing more that needed saying between them. And Julia thought those words the best Christmas present she had ever been given in her life.

*I am afraid; and yet
I'll venture it.*
SHAKESPEARE

—————————————————————————6

The holidays passed, and Winter bared her teeth and drove away the sun from the grey, cold sky. The temperature sat for a week at ten below zero, and everything wore a coating of glistening ice.

Julia stayed close to the fire, wrote long letters, read and dreamed, and made plans for a future she couldn't begin to see or anticipate. Perhaps she had known all along this would be her decision—that same sense of the inevitable drawing her on. But after much prayer and fasting, she had decided that following things through to the end meant going to Utah. Something about her seemed unfinished, incomplete. And a voice inside her whispered that Utah would give her the answers.

She had already given her company notice of leaving, so there was plenty of time to train a replacement for her. She was saving scrupulously, organizing her wardrobe, reading everything she could about the West, and appreciating even the ice and the gloom, knowing this would be her last winter at home.

When she told her parents, her father sat on the sofa and shook his head.

"You're twenty-two years old, Julia; we can't stop you." He looked up, his eyes confused and sad. "What have we done to make you want to leave us?"

Julia flew to his side and held him close and tried to explain, or at least to comfort a little. She couldn't bear to think of her gentle father feeling rejected. For a moment a pang of doubt shook her peaceful resolve. But it passed, leaving only a taste of sadness behind.

Her mother had left the room and did not return. But later that night she came to Julia's bedroom. With some apprehension, Julia watched her enter. She sat down on the edge of the bed and gazed at her daughter, her own feelings carefully veiled behind steel-blue eyes.

"We could keep you—we could force you to stay, I suppose. But what good would it do if you aren't happy?"

She paused, struggling now with her cool control. Suddenly Julia thought she seemed old and tired.

"If this is what you want, we won't stand in your way."

Julia nodded and swallowed, her throat feeling suddenly dry and aching with the burden of tears held back.

"Mother." She leaned her head tentatively on the thin, tight shoulder. "I wish I could tell you," she whispered, "how much I love you."

January slid into February, Winter still holding the land in a tight, clenched fist. The rage of the country was briefly no longer the war but Errol Flynn's publicized trial for statutory rape. And while women were trying to bribe themselves onto his jury, President Roosevelt and a new United Nations of twenty-five countries were pledging to sign no separate peace with the Axis. Near the end of January, Roosevelt met with Churchill at Casablanca, Morocco, and there agreed that the ultimate invasion of Europe should be through France, from the west. The war would be continued, they boldly declared, until the "unconditional surrender" of the enemy.

Julia read the news and grew cold inside, feeling ever more removed from the world she lived in.

"Come, Come Ye Saints" and "purple-mountain majesties" seemed far away and thoroughly unrealistic. But Julia set her date and bought her ticket, wrote to Nolan, and started to pack her bags.

February, short and inconsequential, gave way to March, with somewhat longer days and at least the hope that spring would find its way. The date on the calendar grew closer by leaps and bounds now. There was nothing Julia could do to push back the time.

On March 22, a pale, cold morning, she boarded the wheezing train, amid clouds of hissing steam, mists of tears, and farewells that wrenched at her heart. She sat in her seat by the window and waved to her family, feeling the train gather motion and move away. What was she doing? She pressed against the cold window. Where were they now? She saw them, growing smaller in the distance, huddled together, arms upraised. Everything she loved was retreating behind her. Mountains and deserts and strangers waited ahead. Julia choked back the tears and pushed back the doubts, whispered a little prayer, and wondered where the rumble of the wheels would take her.

The corn lands, muddy and fallow, stretched black for a distance. But gradually the landscape began to change. She slept fitfully, chilly and cramped, through the darkened hours. In the morning Nebraska fled by outside her window, sometimes looking much like Illinois with fields and large red barns and white farmhouses. But with each hour, the land became more hilly and began to look very rough and untamed.

Julia dozed in her seat for awhile; when she awakened, she caught her breath at the scene before her eyes. Far in the distance stretched purple, snow-capped mountains, peak after peak, cloud-dappled or shadow-deep. She stared, her heart growing tight within her. What majesty, what awesome size and strength! She had never in her life seen mountains, and these fulfilled her every expectation.

Wyoming, the conductor told her. Cowboy country. Now every turn of the wheels brought Utah closer! As the hours passed, she spent more time at her window, drinking in the beauty, the newness continually there.

Houses were different here. And so was the land. Trees rose gnarled and twisted to match the landscape, set in fields of pale green sagebrush and scattered boulders. Every mile grew more rocky and more remote. There were no broad rivers here, but tortured, winding gorges where water sprayed and fumed and boiled. Bright flowers clung wherever there was soil, splashes of color from every crevice or crack. Barbed wire fences held back rangy cattle or rough, dark ponies that grazed at dry clumps of grass. Tumbleweeds, sucked against the wires, dotted the fence lines, wizened and withered, or danced and cavorted like crazy, unearthly things. Julia watched their antics, fascinated. It seemed a storybook world stretched out before her, increasing her feeling of vague unreality. Where would she find a place in this kind of world?

The day stretched on. The long hours unwound their burden of waiting, and the train began its approach into Salt Lake. Red sand sprinkled the fields and dusted the mountains—*red* dirt, sprouting stunted cedar and sage. The higher peaks were covered with evergreen forests, and now and then a waterfall boiled down, cutting a swatch of silver against the rock. This was Utah—this was where she had chosen to build an unknown future for herself.

The Union Pacific station was noisy and crowded, the huge trains lined up like huffy, protesting monsters. Dozens of tracks seemed to cross and criss-cross each other. Uniformed Negro porters darted across them, pushing carts burdened with luggage, and calling in rich, echoing voices to one another.

Julia stood on the platform, dazed and bewildered, feeling smaller than she had felt in all her years. Then suddenly a firm hand grasped her elbow and a voice that sounded like music assailed her ears.

"This way, madam. The coach and four is ready. Sorry to keep you waiting."

He tipped an imaginary hat, his playful mouth smiled, and Julia was deliciously safe in Nolan's arms.

He steered her expertly through the crowd and confusion. In the enormous, vaulted station Julia caught glimpses of lavish murals and paintings—one, she was sure, of the railroads' meeting with the historic driving of the golden spike. She could smell stale cigarette smoke and warm coffee, gum and chocolate, and something like bacon and eggs.

They wound their way through the rows of wooden benches, past stacks of piled luggage, over outstretched legs, around small knots of people blocking the way. Dizzy, Julia clung to Nolan's hand, taking three steps to his one and ending up breathless, standing outside, clinging to Nolan's sleeve, trying to catch her breath as she looked around.

The day was dissolving into a lovely evening. Julia noted, with surprise, that the air was mild. She could taste spring with each breath she gulped, and the smell of flowers. And grass—was that freshly-mown grass? She couldn't be sure.

"It's lovely here," she breathed.

"If you say that already, just wait till I've shown you a thing or two!"

Miraculously, her bags had appeared beside them. Nolan

paid the porter and steered for the parking lot. Julia recognized Nolan's car before they reached it. One dear, familiar thing in a new landscape!

Gratefully she slid into the front seat. When Nolan got in beside her, she reached for his hand.

"Nolan, how can I thank you for all you've done?"

"There's a way," he said and gathered her into his arms.

The kiss was light and delicious and non-commital. Nolan drew back and surveyed her with glowing eyes.

"You're lovely, Julia, more lovely than I remembered."

Too lovely to get involved with, he wanted to say. But he tucked the thought back and gave her a brilliant smile.

"Welcome to Zion, Julia," he said.

He drove her all over the city and showed her the sights: the fine houses along the avenues, Capitol Hill, then back through a canyon-like road to the heart of the city, till at last she found herself on Temple Square.

They wandered through the pioneer museum together, sat in the tabernacle and heard the pin drop, and marveled at the tortoise-shell construction. She sat at the base of the Seagull Monument, stood gazing up at the statues of Joseph and his brother, Hyrum. Julia was close to tears more than once. Peace and perfection assailed her on every side. New flowers were planted along the many walks, the trees were budding, the grass was soft and green.

"I left Illinois still locked in winter," she marveled.

"God's country," Nolan reminded her with a grin.

The temple itself, the elegant, powerful lines, sent a thrill through her body she couldn't quite understand. She gazed at the angel Moroni atop the steeple, golden and gleaming, reflecting the waning sun. In the distance the mountains shone rosy and gold in the sunset. Everything looked washed clean and spread over with peace. She felt it surrounding her, felt it inside herself, too. It set a benediction on her desires and left her feeling less lonely and apart.

She had arranged through the mail to stay with a family Nolan knew—actually, his best friend's mother and younger sister. They had an extra room they would let to Julia. She was aware of the Mormons' notorious hospitality but was determined to pay her own way from the very start. So Nolan drove her now to the home of Vera Ogden, down over the viaduct and onto Eighth West, then up a little side street of small, solid houses and into the drive of a tidy brick bungalow.

When Julia met Sister Ogden, what fears she had were settled once and for all. Gentle, lined face, white hair like a halo about her, deep, soft eyes—she was to Julia the image of the gracious, yet motherly woman of Mormon lore. She shooed Nolan away and helped Julia get settled in the pretty, chintz-curtained room which was to be hers. A soft-hued, homemade quilt was spread on the bed, and there were flowers in a vase on an old-fashioned dresser. But, best of all, in the last pale light at the window, Julia could see a view of grey peaks in the distance; here, from her bed, the mountains were framed for her view.

After unpacking, she went down into the kitchen, ate warm pie, and talked for awhile with Vera. It wasn't till later, after a soothing bath, reading in robe and pajamas in her room, that a lively freckle-faced girl burst in upon her.

"Julia, I'm so glad you aren't in bed! Mother said I could only come in if the light was on. I'm so sorry I wasn't here when you arrived!"

Celia Ogden plopped down on the bed and surveyed the stranger with laughing, curious eyes.

"Oh, Nolan was right. You are beautiful," she exclaimed.

"Like a lady. Sort of . . . well, elegant, you know."

Julia couldn't help smiling. "You must be Celia," she said.

The girl nodded, and her freckles seemed to bounce with her short, bobbed hair.

"That's right. I should have said so first off," she apologized. "Are you too tired? Do you mind if I stay for a minute?" she asked.

"I'd love it. I've dozens of questions," Julia confided, sensing that Celia was the perfect person to answer them all!

The few minutes stretched into an hour, then nearly two. Julia discovered that Celia was just nineteen, attended the LDS Business College, was in love with three boys, though one was on a mission, one in the service, and the other already engaged. The last child and only girl in a nest of five boys, she was overjoyed at the thought of having a sister, and in her open, almost childish way was prepared to confer both the title and all her pent-up devotion on Julia. Julia was delighted. She liked the girl and was fascinated by her pretty, girlish looks. For, in spite of the sprinkling of freckles, Celia was pretty, in a healthy, vivacious, charming way.

Julia heard all the gossip of the ward, which people to avoid and which to trust. And, most important of all, what boys were available.

"This awful war will make us all old maids!" Celia grimaced. "But then, I suppose *you* won't have much trouble, though it does seem all the best guys are taken by the Army. Why do the handsome ones always want to enlist?"

Julia laughed and shook her head. "I'm sure I don't know."

"There's my brother," Celia went on, "but he's nearly taken. And I don't think you'd be interested, anyway."

She wrinkled up her nose, and her eyes grew wide as she settled them on Julia with a startled expression.

"You didn't come out here to marry Nolan, did you?"

Julia stifled a laugh and said with a serious face. "And if I did?"

"Well, there's nothing *wrong* with Nolan. It's just, well, he's great to have a good time with and all. But he's not the marrying kind, if you know what I mean."

Celia was looking sincerely worried by now.

"I know what you mean," Julia assured her. "I like Nolan. But he's certainly not what I came here for."

What I came here for . . .

Much later, when Celia had gone, when her prayers were said and she lay in the unfamiliar bed, the words came back to trouble her tired mind. *What I came here for . . .* the same old question to plague her. She was here, and yet she still didn't know quite why. *I suppose I'm here to learn how to become a Mormon. And to find*—find what? Herself? A husband? A future?

She sighed and settled under the cozy quilt. She wouldn't worry herself about finding anything. She would live here with the people and the mountains and take things as they came, a day at a time. She refused to plague a silent, taciturn future into unraveling secrets she wasn't ready for.

One day at a time was enough for her to handle. And, on that thought, she closed her eyes and slept.

*　　*　　*　　*　　*　　*

The next few days flew by, and to Julia's surprise she didn't have time to feel lonely or homesick at all. Celia bustled her from one place to another, introducing her to someone new at every turn. They went sightseeing and job hunting together and came home to good hot meals Sister Ogden cooked. She saw more of Nolan than she had expected, met his family and his old girlfriend who lived next door. Nolan lived with Celia's brother, Barry, and two other young men in an apartment. So Julia met "the guys" and was approved—one of them being the engaged boy Celia was in love with.

Everything was fun and warm and friendly, and Julia soon felt a part of this new world. The days warmed, and the flowers continued to grow. Each morning Julia opened her eyes to a picture of cloud and sun and mountain that dazzled her mind, keeping alive the feeling of magic within her.

Characteristically, it was Nolan who found her employment. Using his first-hand knowledge of her skills and background, and employing his own salesmanship and charm, he arranged an interview and, before she knew it, she had been offered a position as assistant manager at the huge office of *Utah Ice and Storage.* Now she had a place and security, a routine to her days.

So the flurry of the first days began to subside, and a new pattern emerged to fill her life. March warmed into April, and with April came the general conference of the Church. Julia watched the city fill up with people. Even in wartime the Saints poured into Salt Lake, camping in parks, staying with relatives, making do any way they could find, just to be part of the spirit of these few days.

After waiting in line with Celia outside the great doors, Julia found herself seated inside the tabernacle, high in the balcony, looking down on the throng below, feeling part of something much grander than herself. She stood in that sacred place with the rest of the Saints and sang "The Spirit of God Like a Fire," and felt the burning course through the depths of her soul. For the first time in her life she witnessed a prophet speak to his people and bless them with his love. And in those moments something fused within her. From that point on she was no longer a stranger; these were her people, this place was home to her.

She wrote to her parents and tried to describe her life here, frustrated at her inability to capture in words the beauty and joy that were part of her every day. Yes, there were times she was lonely; yes, she was homesick. But life here was a living, growing thing. She felt herself expand and grow inside, and she knew the delight that inner growth can bring.

Even the war seemed different out here in the West. Closer, yet somehow not as dire and depressing. The spirit of patriotism ran very deep, yet was less talked about, less publicized. Utah had more than her quota of volunteers—the Mormons in their usual quiet, efficient way supporting what needed supporting, doing what needed to be done.

Julia noticed a change in women's fashions. The influence of California could be seen as more women were wearing casual slacks, short bobbed hair and skirts above the knees. Yet here there was always the old, conservative element, and Julia's more careful, feminine way of dressing looked beautifully in place.

She worked at her job and liked it, met new people, and attended the ward with Celia regularly. If sometimes a week went by without Nolan appearing, well, she told herself, that was just what she had expected. She happened to see him once walking into an ice cream parlor, a long-legged blonde hanging onto his sleeve and laughing. She saw Nolan turn and flash his beautiful smile, and the girl leaned close and whispered into his ear. It disturbed her to watch that typically "Nolan" scene and upset her that she could be disturbed by something she knew existed all along.

Celia told her the tall blonde's name was Sally.

"She's been trying to land Nolan for longer than you'd

want to know. Since way before Chicago." She shook her curls and wrinkled her freckled nose. "Sally's flashy, but she hasn't got what it takes."

With her thus dismissed, Julia set about trying to forget this Sally, but whenever she thought of Nolan, her face was there. The next time Nolan called, Julia gave an excuse to not see him; she was surprised when he called again within a few days. Still not sure how she felt about being with him, she agreed to see him that night.

When he came, he seemed to pick up where they had left off, as though no change, no time had elapsed between them. He asked with genuine interest about her job, her ward, her life with Celia and her mother. They dined at the choicest seafood spot in the city, and he entertained her with his usual lively wit.

After dinner he told her he had a surprise to show her and drove to a spot near the capitol called Gravity Hill. He explained how a large magnet at the very top of the building was situated to create a phenomenon. Then he drove to the top of the hill and started down.

After a few feet, he stopped the car, slid the transmission into neutral, and sat back with a grin. Julia watched incredulously as the car began inching, bit by bit, back *up* the hill. She watched the bushes pass by, looked down into the canyon; the car kept climbing its slow way up!

Nolan, seeing her expression, laughed out loud and finally, after much pleading, told her the truth. They had just experienced an optical illusion. The road, which seemed to go clearly down, was really slanted up—though much less steeply than the road alongside—which gave the false impression of a downhill slant that wasn't really there. Julia found that explanation nearly as hard to believe as the magnet story and delighted Nolan with her incredulousness.

Why could he make everything so much fun? Julia decided it would be very childish to cut him out of her life entirely. She had accepted him before for what he was. She musn't lose perspective and spoil it now. So she thanked him for the evening and told herself firmly that she must remain content with brief sprinklings of Nolan's enchantment in her life.

A subtle pressure was working upon her slowly. She couldn't quite put a name to it at first. But as the weeks passed, she began to feel slightly awkward, slightly *old,* in a very unflattering way. Looking around her, watching the young people and the families, she realized at last what the culprit was. Most Mormon girls were married before they reached twenty—young, blooming girls snatched up as eager wives. A single, working girl over twenty-two with no attachments and no prospects was rather an oddity. She laughed it off, but the pressure was there to stay.

So when the spring days began to mellow into summer, Julia found herself feeling restless and at loose ends. Marc had written one or two terse letters; her parents' letters were also distant and detached. Nolan was, as always, erratic in his attentions. And Celia had been right about Mormon boys. The good ones seemed already taken, by women or war. Those left behind were young, fresh-faced and awkward. She couldn't see losing her head over one of them. For years she had been used to a man's attentions; a handsome, charming man to fuss over her. She felt superfluous, empty, unimportant now. In simpler terms, she felt sorry for herself.

Thus when Celia came to ask, for the hundredth time, if Julia would consider dating this marvelous guy—just once—a double date with Celia and Fred, she took a deep breath and said, 'Yes.' What could she lose? Summer was coming, the nights would be sweet and mild. Just to dress up and go someplace would be nice. It didn't matter what the boy was like. They'd be going to Saltair on the train, by moonlight. She could look young and pretty and laugh and feel happy again. *Anything could happen,* she told herself, and pushed away doubts that threatened to dampen her spirits. Romance and enchantment begin in one's own heart; Julia would keep hers warm and alive and believing.

Is't possible?—'Tis true:
There's magic in the web of it.
SHAKESPEARE

7

T he boy was as bad as anything Julia could have imagined —worse than her memories of early high school dates. Johnny: tall and awkward, all ears and elbows, a wide-mouthed grin, and a very unflattering hounddog expression in his deep, liquid eyes. When he stared at her, Julia felt her skin crawl. She glared at Celia and slid to the far end of the bench, squashed up against the train window, wondering how she could stick out the next few hours.

Luckily, Celia kept conversation going, and Julia, whenever she could, turned away from the group and watched the land giving way to sagebrush, then salt flats. The wind ran cool, tickling fingers through her hair. She closed her eyes and drew in the breath of the water and salt.

The lavish Moorish pavilion rose up before them, the onion-like domes catching gleams of the evening sun. "Try To Sink!" the signs on the bath houses blinked and challenged, and the train coughed and rumbled over the pilings and came to a stop.

Rising in white and gold splendor above the lake, its nine acres of concrete floor resting on seven thousand wood pilings, Saltair sprawled and twinkled and sang in the lake-cooled night. Julia climbed the tiers of stairs in a dream-like daze, refusing Johnny's arm, floating along, drawn by the Pied Piper lure of the music and lights.

The dance hall appeared and stretched endlessly before her: polished wood flooring laid over the concrete foundation— 140 by 250 feet—outlandish proportions, arched without pillar, blinking and throbbing with subtle, star-soft light, washed with music that warbled and whispered inside her head.

She went into Johnny's arms without even thinking, moving with the waves of sound, formless and free. When the music whispered and shuddered, then started to die, she let Johnny lead her away from the crowded floor to a place at the side where a wet breeze blew the sunset into her face.

"Isn't it magnificent, Julia? I knew you'd like it!" Celia twittered and glowed beside her. "In its heyday ten thousand people danced here each night. I'm glad it's not that crowded anymore. I could barely breathe in there!"

She loosened her fine lace collar and beamed at Fred, who flashed her a smile in return.

"I'm just dying of thirst. Do you think you could find something, Freddie?" Celia blinked her eyes and tilted her pretty head.

"Sure. Come on, Johnny. We'll rustle up something to drink. You ladies stay here. We'll be back, so don't go away."

He winked at Celia, turned, and swaggered off. Julia heard them and saw them dimly, as through a dream. Celia poked her gently, leaned close and giggled.

"Look at all the soldiers! Oh, Julia, don't those uniforms simply melt your heart?"

"Hush, Celia," Julia whispered. "Please leave me alone. I— I'd like to just watch the sunset alone for awhile."

Julia moved a few steps away before Celia could stop her. The beauty was almost too much for her to bear. Some starved spot in her soul was swelled by this beauty, and Celia with her light, airy chatter was spoiling it all.

She moved further along the railing, watching the sunset, enjoying the bright splashes of crimson that stained the sky, trailing into wisps of pale rose and soft pink, diffusing the grey of the water, the pale night air, brushing the seagull's wings with a rosy glow.

She sighed and stared and lost herself in the beauty—until she felt warm flesh brush up against her own.

She turned. The man was staring at her intently. Warm brown eyes, flecked with red and gold. He was leaning over the railing as she was doing. But she knew he had not been watching only the sunset.

"It's too beautiful," she said softly. "It makes me ache inside."

She spoke to the deep eyes, knowing they understood. He nodded. Then turned to gaze with her awhile. The music trailed out, winding cool, trembling fingers around them.

"Will you dance?" he asked, and not waiting for reply, took her arm lightly and led her onto the floor. Her skin burned warm where his fingers rested against it. In his arms the dream seemed real, the wonder inside her rose up and found expression.

For the longest time he held her but didn't speak. At last, as the music wavered and threatened to die, he drew back a little and smiled into her eyes.

"You must have a name, Cinderella."

"Julia," she whispered.

"Julia," he repeated, "I'm Alex Hutton." He paused, then added, "I haven't seen you here before, have I?"

She shook her head, clinging wildly to the magic that seemed to dissolve as the music echoed away.

"Are you," he hesitated, "alone?"

She shook her head again, feeling cold inside.

"Sadly, neither am I." His smile was wistful.

"I—I must get back. They'll be looking for me," Julia said, feeling something within her die as she spoke the words.

"I'll return you then to where I found you."

He took her arm. Before she knew it, she stood again at the railing, staring with burning eyes at the fading sky.

"Julia, there's someone looking for me, too." He turned her to face him. "I'll dance with you again."

The words were a promise that trembled into the air, rose with the night wind and brushed against her cheek.

He turned and was gone, taking the magic with him, and the sunset dissolved and nothing was left but the night.

"Julia, where have you been? We've been looking for you! Here—take this before I spill it all over my dress."

Celia thrust a cup of punch into Julia's hand, then drew her back to where the two boys were standing.

Julia choked down the punch and smiled and laughed with Celia. Johnny watched her with adoration in his eyes. But when he wanted to dance, she hesitated. And when the three of them dragged her, protesting, out onto the floor, and she felt his hand pressed, clammy, against her back, a feeling of angry revulsion rose within her. How dare he spoil the perfection, the dream? She danced across the floor, not looking up—not wanting Alex Hutton to see her while she was with Johnny.

She felt miserable and ashamed of herself as well. Mentally she gave herself a scolding. *Don't act like a naive schoolgirl,* she chided. *It was a brief, fanciful encounter, nothing else. If you weren't so stupidly dreamy and romantic, you'd know that and not make a fool of yourself.* But the harsh words didn't help or stop the hurting that stubbornly beat at her heart.

The minutes wore on, tortuous and taunting. She caught no glimpse of Alex in the crowds. No one seemed to tire with the hours. The music grew loud and harsh; the air grew chilly. Once Julia slipped away and stood by the railing. But the night air clung to her, muffled and damp. She shivered and rubbed her cold arms, but nobody came. And Celia at last dragged her back to the lighted hall.

After that there was only the waiting left until Fred and Johnny decided to leave. Weary and grateful, Julia hurried back to the train. The night seemed drained of beauty and romance. She knew the sky was strewn with a thousand stars, but they didn't shine and sparkle for her. Off in the distance she heard a strain of laughter. Glancing instinctively, she saw a girl—warm blonde hair, a lithe and graceful shape. And with the girl, helping her into a long cream and brown Packard convertible was a man with gentle hands and golden eyes.

She couldn't be sure. It was dark; it was only a feeling. In a moment the car door closed, and he disappeared.

But for the first time all evening Julia no longer felt pretty. She bit her lip and held back the childish tears, and huddled in the welcome dark against the cold window. Why did she get so caught up in her own girlish dreams? Why could a stranger turn promise into ashes and take all the meaning and color out of her life?

* * * * * *

Four days later the impression of sadness still lingered. Julia went to work as usual, riding the bus home from the red brick Utah Ice building down the pleasant, still-warm streets to the Ogden's corner. She couldn't help remembering last summer. How right Marc had been. It was the last. The last farewell to youth, to innocent pleasure, to an entire way of life for her. Life had never been hard like this before—vague and confusing and filled with nameless longings. Her mother would probably say, "You're just growing up." She missed her mother and suddenly felt tired and lonely.

She walked slower than usual from the bus stop to the house, reluctant for some reason to go inside and face even Vera Ogden's sweet, placid greeting. She didn't understand her sudden aversion to people, to confrontations of any kind.

Today, of all days, Celia was waiting, beaming at her from her perch on the old porch swing.

"It's about time you got here. You're ten minutes later than usual." Celia bounced over and grabbed Julia's hand with little-girl anxiety.

"Are you all right?" she asked, her face growing concerned and clouded. "You look tired, Julia, and even a little pale."

Julia smiled; how could she be angry with the girl?

"Come on, sit down. I'll get you some fresh lemonade."

Celia disappeared inside, but was back in a moment with two tall, icy glasses. Julia sipped hers gratefully, feeling herself relax. Celia watched her and, for some reason, her bright eyes sparkled.

"Just a minute, Julia. I'll be back with something better."

Celia disappeared again, then returned in an instant with something held, hidden, behind her back.

"I can't wait any longer," she cried. "Here, this came for you."

She thrust something into Julia's arms—a light, cone-shaped package that crinkled at her touch. Flowers. Julia tore back the paper. One dozen white roses, gleaming pearly and dainty against a bed of green leaves.

"Who is it? Who sent them? Open it!" Celia cried, thrusting the small envelope with her name printed on it into Julia's hand.

Julia could feel her stomach beginning to churn. She slipped out the card. In neat, bold-lettered writing the message read: "To Cinderella, with regrets and fond regard. Alex Hutton."

Down inside, somewhere past the dull pain, a deep joy broke forth.

"How romantic! Julia, whoever is Alex Hutton?"

Julia buried her face in the roses; the magic was there. How had he found her? Could he possibly really care?

Celia hovered, at least wise enough to be still for a moment. Julia looked up, her eyes more alight than she knew.

"Come with me while I put them in water. I'll try to explain."

"Well, how did he find you?" Celia asked moments later, when she had heard the intriguing story. "No wonder you were so strange and moony that night. Julia, do you think he'll call? Do you think he'll come over?"

Those were questions Julia hardly dared ask herself. She escaped with a shake of her head and a little shrug. And Vera, wisely, kept Celia from capering after.

Alone in her room she let her feelings run rampant, indulging every fancy inside her head. She stretched out on her back and gazed at the cluster of mountains that rose like shining parapets in the blue. Spires of some sky-locked castle, bold and remote, they stood out in regal dominance against cloud and air. Her spirit lifted with the sight; her spirit was part of the beauty. Any man who could stir such awareness in her, compel her with such a power—what must he be? She closed her eyes and breathed in the smell of the roses and wondered what Alex Hutton would mean in her life.

She plucked two of the roses and took them to work the next morning, setting them in a small vase where she could see them. About mid-morning a young boy came into the office, wearing some kind of a messenger's uniform. He approached Julia and held out a plain white envelope.

"Miss Julia Wilde?" He spoke with practiced formality.

She took the letter and smiled, and he stood aside, folding his hands stiffly at his back. She glanced at him and raised her eyebrows in question.

"I'm to wait for an answer, miss."

Julia opened the letter, slid out the paper, unfolded it and read:

> Mr. Alexander Hutton cordially requests the pleasure of your company this Friday evening. If this is convenient and you are agreeable, please sign below to acknowledge your acceptance. Mr. Hutton will collect you promptly at seven on Friday.

Below the message her name was neatly typed with ample space for a signature above. She bit back a smile and tried to look very casual as she drew out a pen and carefully signed her name. When she handed the envelope back to the boy, he bowed briefly and formally.

"Thank you, miss." His expression never changed.

Julia watched him walk out the door and disappear down the street. Where did he come from? Was he hired for just this occasion? Or did Alexander Hutton really have his own personal messenger boy?

Alex Hutton the playboy, the debonair, the clever? Perhaps she was only one on a list of girls—classy brunettes and dazzling blondes and sultry red-heads—who all existed for Alex Hutton's pleasure. Perhaps when she saw him in broad daylight, the magic would shatter. He would be smart and smug and really quite ordinary.

She told herself these things, but her heart said no. She had seen too much when she gazed in the rust-brown eyes. She had heard too much in the voice that had spoken her name.

Thursday morning. Nearly two days of waiting. How would she ever fill the cruel hours ahead? She turned to a stack of work and attacked it wildly, glad for the chance to immerse herself and forget, knowing she dared not think too much about Friday.

Julia was ready and waiting long before seven. To keep herself from hovering by the window, she did her nails, re-arranged Alex's roses, touched up her make-up, and again combed her loose, curled hair. Two minutes before the hands on Vera's old mantle clock stood at the hour, she heard the car pull up in front of the house. Amid flurried assurances from Celia and Vera, she answered the sound of the knocker and opened the door.

Alex stood there. Julia's heart caught in her throat when she saw him. The eyes were the same, the hair, the gentle smile—the magic which had engulfed her six nights before.

Somehow she made it through the next few minutes: polite introductions, more polite farewells, walking with him down the path, feeling his hand resting lightly against her arm, somehow making it into the long, cream-colored car, smelling the leather, feeling her own trembling inside. Then Alex was there beside her. The big engine purred into life at his touch. The car inched away from the curb and began to move forward.

She glanced at him. He turned, and the deep eyes answered. And suddenly all the butterflies melted away. She was at home again, in a strange, inexplicable way, as she had been with him by the railing, watching the sunset.

"I'm so filled with questions I don't know quite where to begin."

Her words sounded small and tentative in the stillness.

"You look very beautiful this evening, Julia. And there's only one question. Are you ready to taste the most succulent meal of your life?"

"You must know at this point I'd be ready for anything."

His laughter was short and deep, almost musical.

"Aren't you going to tell me then how you found me? Or why? Or anything?"

Julia's voice was too earnest. He turned with one long look.

"I'll tell you, Julia. But there's one thing I want to know. By any chance have you missed me as much as I've missed you?"

If it weren't for his eyes, she would have laughed at his question—taken it as a light, flattering quip. Instead she answered him honestly, from her heart.

"Incredibly, Alex, yes, I have."

He sighed and seemed to relax at her answer, as though everything that needed to be spoken was spoken between them now. As he wound the car in and out of the evening traffic, he answered the questions uppermost in her mind.

"First I must apologize," he told her, "for not claiming the dance I promised you Saturday night."

Julia felt her skin go hot and turned to the window, hoping he could not see her face.

"It was a promise made on the impulse of the moment," Alex continued. "When I got back to my party I realized how impossible it would be. But I looked for you, and when I finally spied you, I recognized one of the young men you were with."

"Which one?" Julia asked, her curiosity growing.

"The one with your crazy friend. The one named Fred. I wasn't quite sure, but I knew I had seen him before. So I followed my hunch."

He turned, his smile seeking hers. "And I came up lucky. He happens to work for me."

Julia stared. "He works for you?" she repeated.

"That's right. In the new south wing, in a department that's only been open a very short while. I don't know many of the men there yet. But I knew I'd seen him before, and I was right. It took a little searching, but I found him."

He scanned her face. "I know. It's dreadfully unromantic. No fleet-footed couriers searching throughout the kingdom. No trumpets, no grand rewards for discovery of the unknown maiden."

Julia couldn't help smiling.

"You made up for that with the flowers and with your quaint carrier boy and his message."

"You liked that?"

He smiled. A hopeful, boyish smile that made him look younger. He slowed the car and pulled into a tree-shaded lane, through a wide stone arch where an iron eagle hovered. The air grew cooler. Alex slowed the car; she could hear the crunch of loose gravel beneath the tires. A night bird called, hauntingly clear and sweet. The trees thinned into a broad stretch of manicured lawns, bordered by gardens and criss-crossed by wide brick pathways, with arbors and benches and fountains scattered throughout.

"Alex, how lovely! I didn't know this existed."

For a moment the trees were a painful reminder of home: the trees and the lush green growth and the summer-sweet silence.

They dined in the white-pillared building, at linen-draped tables, with candlelight and waiters in shiny tuxedoes. It was part of the dream—to be sitting here with Alex, swept up in the beauty and wonder he seemed to create. And yet it seemed the most natural thing to be doing, as though she had known him forever—for more than her life—as though only with him was her own existence completed.

They talked of books, of people, of ideas, of the music of Beethoven, Wagner and Franz Liszt. They discovered each other and liked the things they discovered. Beethoven dissolved into Alex's piano training, Byron and Keats into Julia's work on the high school paper, and every subject became personal in the end.

"So you come from the corn lands. I come from back East, myself. Though I don't remember much before California."

"If your home's in California, then why are you here?"

"I suppose you could say I'm here because of the war."

The first vague shadow trembled across their evening.

"My father owns businesses scattered throughout California, but he's always wanted to expand into other states. Since the war, Salt Lake has become quite a strategic industrial center. So, of course, that gave him the in he'd been looking for."

"I didn't realize that at all," Julia responded.

Alex nodded. "Dozens of new industries have sprung up here in the last two years, tripling the work force, adding millions of new dollars to the economy. Have you seen the Remington plant?"

Julia nodded.

"That's government grant—thirty million dollars to build it. A contract of eighty-six million for operations. Did you know there are ten major military bases centered in Utah? Hill Base alone employs fifteen thousand civilians, as well as, oh, five or six thousand military personnel."

"I had no idea." Julia was sincerely astounded.

Alex grinned. "Most people don't. It's my business to know. And actually, what I'm doing is small stuff, really. Have you heard of Wasatch Tool and Dye?"

"Yes, I have! I've even been past it once or twice. Is that . . . do you . . ."

Julia stumbled over how to say it.

"If you mean do I own it, not really. My father does. He sent me here as a glorified apprentice. See how I could manage a place on my own."

"And are you passing his approval?"

Alex shook his head, and the deep auburn highlights in his hair seemed to catch fire and gleam in the uneven glow of the candles.

"A strong yes in some ways . . . and a very strong no in others."

A shadow seemed to cross his face and pull the fine lines tighter as he continued.

"My efficiency and productivity figures he can't argue with. They're higher than anyone anywhere else is getting."

Julia felt a sudden, personal pleasure at his words, as though his triumph were somehow her own.

"Of course, I know one of the reasons for my success, which my father could never understand. Which is, in fact, the reason for his displeasure."

"You're talking in riddles," Julia protested.

"I'm sorry." Alex's smile was both sad and gentle. "It's simple, really. My workers are Latter-day Saints. Taught to give an honest day's work for an honest day's pay. Quick, intelligent, honorable men and women, they respond to fair treatment and far out-produce their counterparts in any other area of the country."

Julia nodded. "You were smart enough to discover that and use it. Don't tell me that's what your father objects to?"

94

"In a roundabout way, yes."

Alex sat silent a moment, and Julia watched him. His eyes, which mirrored his soul, were dark and distressed now. Julia felt drawn to his pain, pulled in by the deep, burning eyes.

"You might say I was too impressed by the Mormons. After a few months I started asking questions—a very dangerous thing to do around here."

His mouth flickered in the shadow of a smile.

"I visited Temple Square; I bought a *Book of Mormon*. All at once I found myself meeting with missionaries. One thing led to another, so naturally . . ."

He paused. Julia felt herself holding her breath.

"You began to believe. You wanted to be a Mormon."

"Yes." Alex looked at her intently as he continued. "I told my father I wanted to be baptized. He informed me it was absolutely out of the question. I persisted. He forbade me wrathfully."

The sad, wry smile returned to Alex's face.

"Were you baptized anyway?"

"Yes," Alex replied.

"And what of your mother? How did she feel and react?"

A shadow crossed over his face that made Julia shudder.

"I wish I knew. I've wondered so many times. You see, my mother's been dead since I was a child."

"Oh, Alex!" Why could his words cause such pain within her?

He smiled—a lonely, melancholy smile.

"I was only five years old. I barely remember. A few little things here and there." He shrugged his shoulders. "You know, a favorite song, an expression or two."

He paused, then made some decision and went on.

"I can remember what it was like when she touched me. . . when she tucked me into bed at night."

Julia choked back tears and a longing to hold him. Instead she leaned forward and placed her hand over his, feeling the lean, warm strength of his fingers.

"Is it still hard sometimes? Even with all the years?"

His eyes searched hers as they had the night of the sunset—deep and honest, kind and safe.

"Yes, yes it is. Perhaps if my father had remarried."

Julia held his gaze, wanting him to continue.

"But after Mother—well, no one could fill her place. His work had always been important to him, so he lost himself in it. He was lucky to find a good housekeeper when I was small. In some ways she's been more or less like a mother. It's worked out . . . all right . . ."

His voice trailed into the stillness. Unconsciously Julia played with his hand as he spoke. *All right. But all right's not good enough for you, Alex!* She thought the words, but what did she dare say? That she longed to mother him and mother his children? That she longed to fill the void and bring love to his life?

"Anyway, it's been over ten months since I was baptized." Alex's mouth curved with a grin that spread into his eyes. "I'm still here; none of my father's dark threats have materialized."

"How do you think he feels about it now?"

Alex stirred and sighed. "I don't know, Julia. After his initial anger faded, I don't think he knew what to do. I'd never really opposed him before. I think he's convinced himself it's a passing fancy—a boyish attachment I'll grow out of in time."

Julia raised her eyebrows. "Oh dear," she breathed. "He couldn't be more wrong, could he?"

A little glimmer returned to Alex's eyes. "How do you understand so well?" he asked her.

"Because I've been through something so similar," she said.

His deep eyes filled with instant interest. She told him the story of the past year of her life, beginning with the evening in Chicago. The warm eyes searched her face, they never wavered. She told him things she had never spoken before, feelings she never had dared share with another. And as soon as she spoke, she knew that he understood. She could feel his spirit mingling with her own.

They left the table and walked through the grounds and gardens. There still was so much to say; the minutes flew. He plucked a pale pink rose for her, and she breathed in its fragrance so that ever after the sweet, frail scent of roses would remind her of the wonder of that night, when she learned what it was to discover yourself in another, to see your own soul mirrored in someone else's eyes.

When at last he drew up to her house, it was well after midnight. He apologized.

"Sister Ogden will understand," Julia assured him.

"That's good to know, since I don't understand myself."

Julia felt a thrill, a tremor of joy pass through her.

"I've never felt anything like this in my life," he said.

The brown eyes sought hers, but she dropped her gaze before them. At the door he brushed her cheek with his lips and held her against him for one brief, gentle moment.

"Julia."

Her name was like poetry when he spoke it. This feeling between them was more than she could bear. She had loved before, she had known the press of desire. She had never felt these feelings that swept her before.

He left her. She wanted to call out, to draw him back to her. It was painful to watch him go. Yet once inside, she felt as though his presence still was with her, enmeshed in the very fiber of her being.

Long after she slid into bed she lay there and wondered.

She was accustomed to long, slow relationships in her life. Nolan had changed that; had changed her whole life for her. But her relationship with Nolan, the Church, her conversion— even they seemed slow compared to this. She had loved Alex Hutton since first she laid eyes upon him—a fairy-tale concept she'd given no credence to before.

But how does one deny feelings as deep as her feelings? Ignore truth when you see it shining from someone's eyes?

I will yield to thee; Love for thy love,
and hand for hand I give...
SHAKESPEARE

8

T he next morning was Saturday, and Celia, of course, was
waiting, anxious to hear all about the night before. Julia
was tempted to answer her simply: "I went to dinner, and
talked, and discovered the man I love. The man I am going to
love for the rest of my life."

She laughed, imagining Celia's varied reactions, and tried
to speak sanely about something too bright, too uncommon
for words. She helped clean the house, grateful for chores to
do. She didn't feel young and giddy and excited but different
somehow, in a deep, alarming way.

Mid-afternoon the telephone rang. It was Alex.

"I've missed you," he said. "Is there any way I could see
you? Tonight, perhaps?"

"Of course. What time?" she asked.

She could hear the relief in his voice as they set the details.
She wondered what he was reading in her own.

They ate, by mutual agreement, in a small, cozy restaurant.
The meal was superfluous, something they barely noticed.
They walked in a park, then drove up into the canyons, where
the shadows of night were already beginning to stretch.

Being together was intensely exciting and yet so natural.
The more they talked, the more there was to say. They stood
on a wooden bridge and gazed down at the water, listening to

the creek murmuring softly beneath their feet, breathing the heady breath of the mountain air.

"This is crazy," Alex said. "I never imagined. I . . . there's a 'girl back home' I'm supposed to marry. You know, one of those things assumed before we were out of diapers."

Julia smiled and told him of Marc, with no pain in the telling.

"Do you love him still?" he asked when she was done.

"There are so many kinds of love." She searched for expression. "I care for him still but not in a vital, essential way."

She wanted to add, "I've never cared for anyone as I care for you. As though you were part of my breath, part of my being."

But that was the one thing that neither of them had said, sensing that once it was faced, it would be all-consuming; once it was stated there would be no way of going back.

When he brought her home, they made plans to meet in the morning, for the Choir broadcast on Temple Square. The next morning they sat close together on one of the wooden benches, surrounded by music, feeling tradition and beauty and peace sweep over their souls. He took her slim hand and held it in his hands, gently. And Julia's heart swelled with the music and much, much more.

After the broadcast they walked where the Saints had walked, wandering the lovely square Brigham had planned, where four days after the Saints pulled into the valley he stuck his cane in a spot of untouched ground and stated, with his usual emphatic enthusiasm, "Here we will build a temple to our God." Before them stood the reality of that vision. And within them, too, the vision grew and sang.

"Aren't you overdoing this a little?" Celia asked her later, as they walked home from sacrament meeting in the mellow evening dusk. Vera, walking with them, smiled and shook her head.

"Leave Julia alone, dear. This is something you don't understand."

Julia glanced at the older woman and found a warm sympathy in her eyes. It strengthened her, somehow, to know this consuming feeling, this power that swept her being could be natural and right.

Monday morning she arrived at the office early. But already waiting were flowers with her name on them. The card read "To my love" with Alex's signature.

She moved through the day with automatic motions, performing her tasks with practiced efficiency. "Preoccupied" ... "dreamy" ... the other workers teased her. She had never felt anything like this before. Alex pervaded her every thought, her every action. She was lost in a world that was Alex, where nothing else mattered, where nothing had power to break the pervading spell.

The day seemed long and confining, almost boring. When the hands of the clock reached five, she was ready to go. She stepped outside, and Alex's Packard was waiting along the curb. He was leaning against the side, languidly waiting. The sight of him filled her with joy that was almost a pain. He nodded briefly, though the deep brown eyes were sparkling.

"May I assist you, madam?" He reached out and took her hand. But he stood there, pressing her fingers, neither one moving. How much he wanted to take her into his arms!

"This has been the longest Monday of my life," he murmured.

She nodded. "I know," she whispered.

He opened the door and carefully helped her inside, his hands when he touched her impressing her skin with a cool and gentle caress.

They stopped at a drugstore phone booth so Julia could call Vera, and then they spent the evening together. The hours flew. They talked and drove as the day cooled into twilight. He took her to his apartment, one side of a white frame duplex set back on one of the twisting avenue streets. There was no one about; they sat on the porch together, and he showed her boyhood momentoes. She got him to talk a little about his work and his family, though that was a subject they usually seemed to avoid.

"Why did your father let you stay here?" she asked him. "After you joined the Church, I mean?"

Alex fingered the leather volume he was holding, his eyes troubled and searching.

"I'm not sure. As I've told you, my father's not easy to figure out. His sense of pride—maybe even a sense of justice. He knew there was nothing to fault about my work."

"But his chances of pulling you back, away from the Church, would be so much less here."

"Perhaps it was simple—he didn't have anyone qualified to replace me."

Julia smiled, and his warm eyes answered and lingered and held hers.

"I haven't known many women," he said, very softly. "A few—of my father's choosing mostly. I can't remember . . ."

He paused, and the chestnut eyes, burning and flecked with color, hesitated. Julia held her breath. A brown thrush called from the house eaves, shrill and insistent.

"I've never felt really safe with a woman before. Does that sound strange?"

She shook her head, scarcely moving, yearning toward him, hoping that he could feel.

"There've been girlfriends, of course, but that was all show and surface. I've never known what it's like—the warmth of a woman near."

102

There were tears in her eyes. Alarmed, Julia tried to check them. But one rolled down unbidden; she brushed it from her cheek.

"Julia!"

He was instantly beside her. She started to look away, embarrassed. But something stopped her and held her. She reached up and touched his face.

"I've needed you all my life, without even knowing."

"Yes," she replied, afraid of the truth no longer. "I think I was always meant to belong to you."

She was in his arms. For the first time he really held her. His lips sought hers, and the tenderness mingling with passion shook them and bound them together with startling force. She thought she had loved; she thought she had given in loving. But in this first long kiss, something opened within her soul, and she thought she would perish from joy and longing.

He released her and drew back, trembling.

"Alex!" she whispered.

He kissed her again, and this time, when he was through, he held her against him and stroked the soft head on his shoulder and felt her gentle breath as it rose and fell, and whispered her name and kissed the smooth line of her cheekbone, and tried to control the joy and the aching desire— the wonder of holding this woman within his arms, the knowledge that life would be futile unless she was with him; unless she could be forever his.

Tuesday he came in the morning and drove her to work. There was almost a shyness between them until he touched her, and she told him with her eyes that she was his. When she came out after work, his car was waiting.

"Julia," he asked her, "could you get a short leave of

absence? A day or two?"

She looked up, confused. "What for?"

"I want to take you home to meet my father."

She drew back. "No," she protested. "I couldn't. It's too soon. Please, Alex."

He took her hand and spoke softly. "Listen, Julia. Periodically my father flies me home. For a progress report. I just got a letter this morning. He wants me to come on the weekend."

She shook her head. "Then go. I won't run away before you get back."

He smiled; his eyes were intensely tender.

"It isn't too soon, and you know it. Julia, Julia. I can't live like this—with you and without you. Near you and yet denied."

A bee droned near the window, then there was silence. No traffic, no people, no presence but Alex's eyes.

"We're not exactly children," he argued. "We've both waited long enough. And this is war time. What reason is there to postpone what both of us want?"

She sighed. She didn't answer. He started the engine, squeezing her hand in his where she let it remain. He drove to Temple Square and stopped the car there.

"Julia," he asked, "will you walk with me a minute?"

She nodded and took his hand when he came round to help her. It was quitting time, and people were going home; it was dinner time, too early for the tourists. The square was peaceful, deserted—their own. It was cool by the fountain and under the tree-spread shadows. The fragrance of flowers was heady on the air. They sat on a bench, and he drew her against his shoulder, his fingers brushing the soft hair back from her cheek. Then he tilted her head till her eyes could not avoid him. She could see the temple in the distance, grey and gleaming.

"Two weeks ago I didn't know you existed." His voice was very gentle, very low. "I had no intentions of falling in love."

He smiled, and the smile sent shivers through her body.

"My life was in order; I thought I was content. Then I happened to stand by a rail to watch the sunset, and see a girl beside me and look into her eyes, and feel something I had never felt before."

The gentle voice became deeper with emotion.

"I love you, Julia."

He paused, and the sweet words lingered.

"In all my dreams I never really knew, I never understood this kind of joy."

He touched her lips just briefly with his own, then spoke against her skin, barely breathing the words.

"Will you marry me, Julia? Will you link your life with mine? It would be my greatest pleasure to make you happy, to spend the rest of my days in loving you."

"I am yours already. How could I answer no?" She kissed his cheek, then spoke against his lips.

"Yes, I will marry you. I love you, Alex. I love you."

The words became lost, became mingled with the kiss that spoke with an eloquence words could never possess. Alone, in a world of peace and promise, love moved with the voice of tomorrow in their hearts.

Tenderly, Alex drew back and reached into his pocket. He opened his hand to reveal a slim gold circle, a ring with a diamond that gleamed in the evening sun, that winked and sparkled with beauty and life of its own.

Gently he slipped it onto Julia's finger, nestling the slim white hand within his own. Julia, incredulous, stared at the gem on her finger.

This is war time, she thought. *People don't get engaged with diamonds. Diamonds like this.*

He was laughing at her gently. "I can see you weren't expecting a diamond. It's all right, Julia. It's real—you can breathe again."

She held out her hand and stared at the radiant beauty. "But, Alex..."

"No, Julia, no protests. It binds you and me together." The joy in his voice sent a tremor of happiness through her. "It stands for how much I love you."

He took her hand and fingered the diamond.

"If you look at it that way," he mused, "it really is quite inadequate, don't you think?"

She laughed, and the sound was sheer joy; she hugged him, she kissed him, she caressed his bright hair, she nestled against his chest. She lost herself in the joy of his love and devotion, in the pleasure she could see in his beautiful eyes.

He took her home, and they spoke no more of his father. Tomorrow would come; for right now there was only today. And this today would be part of forever for them.

When Julia entered the house, both Vera and Celia were sleeping. She sat up late, entering everything into her journal, letting her heart flow through the privacy of her pen.

Then she knelt and tried to express to One other her feelings, overcome by the mark of His hand in her life. What strange events had brought her to this moment! She felt a great surge of love for a Heavenly Father who could move and direct and bless her life this way. Her future was in His keeping and with that assurance, she slept—with a feeling of sweetness and wonder and light.

When Celia saw the diamond, for once she was speechless. Vera Ogden left her work at the kitchen counter and hugged Julia to her, her sweet face radiant with kindness and joy.

"I wish your own mother could be here to share this," she whispered.

"Thank you," Julia replied, her eyes bright with tears. "No one else could take her place as well as you do!"

Most people who saw the diamond at first were overwhelmed. The girls at work hovered about her, while the young men looked awkwardly on.

"That guy with the gorgeous car! He's so handsome," they giggled. "He must be as rich as he looks!"

Julia beamed on them all. She wanted to say, "What matters is that he's Alex. Gentle and kind and intelligent. More of a man than anyone I've met my entire life."

Her happiness had a sense of the unreal about it. So she was glad when Alex appeared at the end of the day—intact, warm, and real, and all was the same between them.

They spent Tuesday evening together, hoarding the hours. Wednesday night Alex had an important meeting. And Thursday Julia had an MIA lesson to teach. Two days apart. That ought to be a small enough matter. But both of them regarded the prospect with pain.

Before the evening was over, the dreaded subject, the trip to California, was finally faced.

"You called and told him?"

"Yes, he knows you're coming."

"But he isn't happy about it."

"I didn't get that impression. To tell the truth, I think he's a little afraid. I've been quite a thorn in his flesh this last little while, continually springing something new upon him."

Alex drew her close. "Julia, please don't worry. I'm afraid I can't make any guarantees about how lovable Father is. But I can promise you this, he'll fall in love with you." He kissed her gently. "He won't be able to help it."

Julia shook her head, her eyes clouded and fearful.

"No, Alex, I've thought about it, and that's not true. I'll be the embodiment of all he resents about you—all that has come between himself and his son."

Alex grew quiet at her words, and the fear in her tightened.

"I never thought of that," he replied. He gazed thoughtfully at her, his brown eyes open and honest. "I won't lie and pretend that isn't a possibility."

"I know," she repeated. "I've been through it with my own parents. He's had nothing to blame so far—not until me."

Alex shook his head. "Don't will it to happen," he warned her. "What makes you so canny and wise, anyway?"

He was teasing her gently; the red-brown eyes were sparkling.

"Maybe you're just what he needs to make him see. To open his eyes—to open his heart."

His voice caressed her, warm with faith and love. She pushed back her fears and smiled at him, determined to be hopeful.

"If anyone has the power to touch him, you do, Julia."

"He's your father, so there must be something special about him. Something wonderful—so I'll go on that premise," she said.

"I love you," he laughed, and the subject for then was abandoned as he held her close and kissed away every fear.

Wednesday Alex drove Julia home from work, and they spent a few moments talking, but that was all. She used the evening preparing for the weekend, deciding on just the right clothes and jewelry to wear to impress this man who held so much power in Alex's life. She worked on her lesson a little but had trouble concentrating.

A letter had arrived from her mother that very day. Twice

she almost sat down to compose an answer. But something stopped her. Something whispered, *wait!* Was happiness like hers too good to be true? Just what was she afraid of concerning this weekend? Or was she only hesitant about how to explain? How to tell her quiet, reasonable parents that she was in love? That she was engaged to a man she had known for less than two weeks?

She threw off all thought and went back to her sorting and packing. She refused to give discouragement a place. She had faith in herself and Alex and their love.

Thursday her lesson went well, and when it was over, she stopped with Celia for ice cream to celebrate. They chattered and giggled together like school girls, and Julia enjoyed it. The last two weeks of her life had been more demanding, more tense than she'd realized.

When they arrived home, Vera reported that Nolan had called her.

"Time for his monthly date," Celia teased.

"I think that was it," Vera confirmed. "I didn't know what to tell him. He said something about calling back, hoping to see you on Friday. I told him I knew you were already busy that night."

Celia laughed. "Oh, Mother! What would he say if he knew?"

Julia wondered. She hadn't thought about Nolan for days. Would he understand when she tried to explain about Alex? For some reason she wanted Nolan to understand.

"He said he'd try to catch you sometime on the weekend. I left it at that . . ." Vera's trailing words sounded uncertain.

"That's fine," Julia assured her. "I'm glad you didn't try to tell him. I'll talk to him next week and tell him myself."

"And he'll realize too late that he's lost you forever!"

Celia cried out the words with a wild, theatrical gesture.

Julia couldn't help smiling.

"I'm sure he'll live through it," she said.

If I can just live through this weekend, she thought to herself, hating the fears and uncertainties that plagued her. It seemed the richer the prize, the higher the price tag, and everything good in life had to be paid for. Nothing worth having was easy or free.

He commanded her with many bitter threats;
Poor wretch, That for thy mother's fault
art thus exposed to loss!
SHAKESPEARE

—————————————————————————————9

It was a small, private plane, Julia discovered, which would take them from Salt Lake to San Diego. She had never flown before, but with Alex beside her her fears became fascinations, and every potential danger became an excitement.

The mountains, bathed in a dozen sunset colors, spread out in massive wrinkles and rises beneath her. She could see the snow-capped peaks through the rose-brushed clouds and the thin lines of rivers that cut in silver across the blue-brown expanse. This was a world for fairy tales and giants, and she sorrowed to see the mountains stretch out and end, leaving nothing but brown, uneven waste below.

At the California airport, a car was waiting, chauffeur driven. The man, in a dark grey suit, greeted Alex warmly and took their bags. Julia sat in the back seat, stiff and uneasy, not wanting to talk with Alex in this man's hearing, feeling already the stranger, the unwelcome outsider.

When they reached the house, the shadows of evening were building, with still little pockets of gloom scattered here and there. The house was set far off the road, up a tree-lined drive. On the grounds were plants and trees Julia didn't know: palms and cacti and peculiar, tropical-looking things. Behind the house and other buildings the landscape sloped, and Julia could see the line where land met water in a violet-blue mass that stretched on to merge with the sky. The house itself was federalist in design, not what she had expected for California, but proper and very dignified—almost forboding.

"Did you grow up here?" she asked Alex.

"Yes. It was built shortly after I was born."

The car pulled to a stop in the gravelly driveway. The engine hummed low, then was silent. The big doors clicked open.

"All those rooms for just one little boy?"

It was easy to picture him, wandering through all that silent, untouched space, lost and lonely, needing a mother's love. He helped her out of the car, and his eyes were shining.

"Stop feeling so sorry for me. I survived."

"Why can you read my thoughts so well?" she asked him.

The chauffeur was back in the car, and it pulled away, leaving them standing alone by the massive brick house.

Alex took her hand and pulled her along beside him. He flew up the broad stairs eagerly, like a boy. Julia forced herself to share his enthusiasm, hoping her face looked pleasant and unstrained, hoping her foolish fears were properly hidden.

Alex pushed open the door and called into the silence.

"Father . . . Maria . . . I'm home. Where is everybody?"

A middle-aged woman appeared at the end of the hall. A long Oriental carpet ran the length of the entry, and Julia discerned a tall Chippendale chest, flanked by chairs, and a stand with a fern draped on it. That was all she had time for before the woman was there.

"Maria!" Alex embraced her warmly. Maria's brown eyes flickered with warmth and pride. Her black hair, pinned in a bun at the nape of her neck, was streaked with grey. Her skin looked weathered. And brown. *Was the woman part Mexican?* Julia wondered. The lines around her eyes were crinkled and deep.

112

"Maria, this is Julia Wilde, my fiancee."

Maria turned and smiled at her graciously.

"Welcome to Point Charlotte, Julia."

Her low voice was gracious, but when she turned back to Alex, pride flashed in her face; the dark eyes caressed him as she spoke.

"Your father awaits you both in the East Room, Alexander."

She moved to address Julia. "Would you like to freshen up?" she asked.

"No, thank you, that won't be necessary," Julia answered, encouraged by how strong and natural her own voice sounded. She knew that Alex was anxious to see his father, and she had no wish to postpone the meeting herself.

Maria nodded slightly, then walked before them. Alex reached for Julia's hand, and she gave it gratefully, glad for the warmth of his flesh against her own.

A wide, curved entrance opened into the East Room, with elaborate carving in wood painted creamy white. As soon as she crossed the threshold, Julia saw him. He was sitting in a wing-backed chair by the fireplace. But he rose as they entered and stood with his hand on the mantel.

He was shorter and a little stockier than Alex. His eyes were deep-set, and they seemed alive in his face. In the hard and disciplined flesh that showed no expression, the burning eyes were all that seemed alive.

He greeted his son, and his rich voice held some warmth in it. Julia watched in fascination as at last he turned his gaze on her.

When their eyes met, she was instantly, pleasantly startled. There was something magnetic that drew her to the man. She could see a response leap up, though he tried to quell it. She smiled into the eyes, feeling a sense of calm and power. With reluctance, with difficulty, he drew back his gaze. But by then she had seen inside him, and nothing else mattered.

After that the evening seemed normal enough. They sat by the fire and chatted; they ate a light meal. Adam Hutton's questions were polite and pleasant. Once or twice she found him gazing at her, a puzzled look, a searching in his face. But when she met his eyes, they dropped before her.

He talked only about surface subjects, or safe ones. The Mormon Chuch never once came up. But then neither did their engagement or their marriage. Now and again Julia perceived a sensation of chill, as though she felt for a moment the strong, hard reins that Adam Hutton held carefully in his hands—not tightened, but watchfully kept, and ready.

When the evening ended, Julia was relieved. At the door of her room, Alex bid her goodnight.

"It's late. I'll let you sleep," he apologized. She knew he felt awkward about following her inside.

"When tomorrow will I see you?" she questioned.

"There's the meeting at seven. You heard Father talk about that. I'm sure we'll be done by noon and have lunch together."

Julia sighed, not knowing the sadness her face revealed.

"You can sleep late, and Maria will take good care of you."

His tone was concerned and soothing. She tried to smile.

"You can swim in the ocean awhile. You'll love it, Julia. The hours will fly, and then I'll be back again."

She hesitated and then decided to ask it.

"Your father didn't say anything. What do you suppose he thinks?"

"Of us?" A little frown creased his forehead. "I don't know. But I'll find out tomorrow," he promised.

He kissed her, not once but several times. She relaxed at his touch, at his love, like a fortress around her.

"Sweet dreams, my love. Remember, I love you, Julia."

She carried his words, his assurance into the room, hugged them to her as she lay in the velvety darkness, trying to read the closed book of tomorrow's hours, trying to second-guess a determined man whose dealings with her had not yet even begun, though the prelude had been enacted years before and would rise, wraith-like, to hover inexorably between them.

Julia didn't sleep late. The bright sun at her window and the sensation of being in a strange room woke her. She showered and dressed and went down to a wonderful breakfast of new-baked rolls and eggs and garden fresh fruits. There was no one in the house but herself and Maria. She was tempted to question the woman but relinquished the impulse, afraid she might do more harm than good.

Instead she asked the way to the ocean and walked down a warm stone path to the sheltered sea, breathing in the sharp air and the mews of the seagulls and the sound of the water which washed to the rocks of her soul, exposing new, almost primitive emotions. *How little I've experienced in life,* she pondered. *There's so much I've never seen or done.*

The feel of the ocean spray was exhilarating, the sound of the waves, the endless variety of color and movement and shape as the water rushed landward, breaking in wild foam that crept up to curl warm and harmless about her feet. How marvelous it would be to walk here each morning, to live with the voice of the ocean in your head and experience this strange mixture of peace and intoxication.

Alex was true to his word. They ate lunch on the terrace— Alex, Julia, Adam Hutton, and two other men, carry-overs from the business meeting that morning. It was a quiet, careful, impersonal affair. As it ended, Alex rose with the others.

"I've got to go over some things with these gentlemen," he

explained to Julia. "An hour or two should do it."

She began to reply, but Adam cut in.

"I'll take care of Julia." His voice was firm and decisive. "She and I have some things that need to be discussed."

So that was how it would be! Alone with the lion. Alex safely removed.

Julia steeled herself, refusing to let her fears outdistance her courage. If that's how the old man was going to play, she wouldn't complain. She smiled, maintaining a calm and gracious manner. She was determined he would not see how she really felt. That was one little edge she had and could keep. It was only an edge; her main weapon was Alex's love. But she hated to think of using his love that way.

Julia walked with the man the short distance to his study, keeping pace with his steps, keeping silent with his silence. As they entered the room, his deep eyes caught and held hers for a long moment before he spoke and offered her a chair. Still his probing eyes kept searching her, sizing her up. She answered the eyes with a growing sense of excitement, every nerve in her body taut and ready for battle, every feeling throbbing close to the surface now.

"Julia. A lovely name for a lovely girl."

He nodded and almost smiled. She inclined her head, keeping her eyes ever steady upon his.

"I appreciate you coming with Alex this weekend. It's fortunate, really. Gives you and me opportunity to meet and expedite this matter a little more quickly."

Her eyebrows shot up, and a tremor pulsed through her being. But she was determined not to speak, not to help him along.

He had been standing. He sat at his desk; their eyes now were level.

"I've never known fancy or delicate ways of speaking. So I

won't embarrass us both by attempting them now."

It seemed to Julia the level gaze was growing colder, and there was no tone, no hint of apology in his voice.

"I have plans for Alex's life, and, until just lately, his own desires for the future have run parallel to mine. As they ought to between a man and his only son."

The heavy eyebrows rose, and the hard brow furrowed. But no other sign of expression crept into his face.

"I made one mistake. That was sending the boy to Utah. I had no idea of this sentimental, religious strain he's displayed, of his weakness to the influences he would meet there."

Julia could feel the distaste in the older man's voice.

"This fascination with Mormonism is only passing."

He paused, and his eyes bore deeper into her now. She perceived them, like points of bright light, and she felt herself tremble.

"And so, my dear, is his fascination with you."

He paused again, that his words might make full impression. There was no hesitation, no feeling in his eyes.

"You see, I have no intention of allowing this unfortunate diversion to interfere with Alex's life and career."

The look came over his face that she had first read as almost a smile. But she realized now the expression was more of a sneer, an irrepressible contemptuous reaction.

"I likewise have no intention of allowing Alex to marry you, Julia."

He was done. He had certainly left nothing unclear or unstated. Julia sat silent a moment, controlling her own response, willing her voice, when she spoke, to be feelingless as his own.

"That all sounds very good, very cold, and very final."

An eyebrow shot up. The hard eyes began to burn.

"But there are a few factors you are not taking into

account. Or perhaps they are things you are totally unaware of."

"Such as?" The cold voice began to sound angry now.

"Such as the simple fact that Alex loves me."

Adam Hutton didn't attempt to control his sneer. It became a very uncomplimentary snort.

"He has known you a matter of weeks. He's infatuated. There is a girl he is going to marry—long since decided."

He was brushing the matter aside, a provoking annoyance.

"Alex isn't a child, Mr. Hutton. He knows what he's doing. Obviously, this 'other woman' is not his choice."

Julia tightened her mouth and held her head high, her gaze level. For an instant a spark of respect shot through the cold eyes.

"I congratulate you, my dear. You're very spunky. But bravado will not win you what you desire. I am still the controlling factor in Alex's life, in all the important ways—the ways that matter."

Julia could feel something seething within her now. Her own eyes were full of fire as she responded.

"Does Alex know you hold him in such contempt? That you have so little respect for his mind or his feelings? You say you know him; you insinuate that you love him!"

The scorn in Julia's tone was real and biting.

"You sadly underestimate your son."

"Don't you presume to tell me about my own son! I have nurtured him and known him for twenty-four years. You are . . ."

"Nothing."

Julia spat out the word like a challenge between them.

"I know you hold me as nothing, of no account. Well, you may have known Alex at one time. You may even know him now—know and understand him. But you are obviously quite

118

ignorant of love."

She paused and her voice grew unconsciously strong and warm. "You know little of the force of real love in a person's life."

He made a move, as though almost to reach out for her, angry and awkward. His eyes were blazing, though the lines of his face were still hard. But his eyes held some new element now besides anger. Something that scathed Julia deeper than his disdain.

"You insult me in my own home. I will not allow it! No woman has ever . . ."

He stopped. His dark eyes grew narrow. He gazed at her, and then angrily shook his head. He pushed back his chair; it scraped on the hard wood surface.

"I can see that you are determined to fight me. You and your Mormon family have dug in your claws and hope to . . ."

Julia's laughter drew him up short.

"My Mormon family! You think there's some kind of a plot here."

Her amusement, so much a relief, was very real.

"I have no 'Mormon family' with designs on your son, Mr. Hutton. If you remember, Alex told you I come from back East. My mother dislikes Mormons almost as vehemently as you do."

The deep-set eyes sunk, smouldering; the dark brow furrowed.

"Your mother? Just where back East?"

"Actually, it's more Midwest. From Illinois. I became a Mormon much as Alex did, sir. Against my parents' wishes and desires."

She smiled unconsciously.

"If my mother were here, she'd be a delightful, intelligent ally, more than happy to take sides with you against me." She arched an eyebrow. "There was a 'boy' in my life, as well. As a matter of fact . . ."

"Have you ever lived in Indiana?"

The interruption, the unexpected question caught Julia off-guard.

"Why, no. Well, my mother was raised in Bloomington, Indiana. But we've never been back there except to . . ."

"Her name. What's her name? Your mother's name?" he demanded.

"Amelia. Amelia Harvey before she was married. She met my father—his family's from Illinois. And so she decided . . ."

Her voice trailed off to nothing. Adam Hutton felt for his chair and sat down heavily. His eyes had grown wide; his expression held horror. Or at least that was the word that crossed Julia's mind as she sat back into her own chair and regarded him.

"Sir, I . . . is . . ."

Julia couldn't understand his alarm, his apparent distress, but she could feel it, like a choking hand, like a clammy chill between them.

He sunk back in his chair, he no longer looked stiff and hardened. Julia shuddered. He was speaking, but under his breath.

"Amelia! Amelia's daughter . . . Amelia's daughter . . ."

She couldn't hear his words, but he sprang up suddenly, his eyes blazing forth like a flame to burn into her own.

"Oh, Amelia! Why do you reach down through the years to torture my life?"

The words were a cry. The words made Julia tremble. She stared at the man; then, suddenly, she knew.

I was just seventeen, and he was a good deal older. Intensely attractive, intensely sure of himself . . . he gave me a ring, a huge diamond surrounded by rubies . . . it was the hardest thing I've

120

ever done in my life . . .

Her mother's words like a gall, like a taunting rang through her head. *It couldn't be.* And yet she knew it was, though her mother had never told her the rich man's name. This was the other man her mother had loved. Adam Hutton was the haughty young man she had nearly married!

"Your mother still wants to destroy me. I should have known it."

What was the man saying? Julia forced herself to focus her concentration.

"Your mother sent you."

The cold accusation swept through her. She wasn't aware she had moved, that she stood beside him.

"No, no. My mother doesn't even know about Alex. She doesn't even know I'm here."

He paused; he was acutely aware of her, of her closeness. He reached out a hand, and then dropped it; his eyes sought her eyes.

"I saw her the first time I looked at you."

The hard voice was quiet. "I merely knew there was something there that I recognized. Whoever would have dreamed . . ."

The sentence hung unfinished, saying so much—so much that he couldn't say!

"Then you knew of me?"

Julia tried to read his expression. She hesitated a little. The arrogant pride—expecting everyone around him to live for him, through him—so much was coming back now, bit by bit. She took a deep breath.

"Not very much, really. In fact, I had never even heard your name."

The deep eyes scowled, but she couldn't read their expression.

"Just this past year my mother told me about you."

"Told you what?" The tone of sheer command made her shudder.

"I asked her if she had ever loved another man."

Julia thought she saw brief pain in the dark eyes that watched her. She couldn't be sure. If it came, it had passed very quickly.

"She told me how she met you, how she loved you."

"Did she tell you she turned me down? What a fool she was!"

Julia felt herself cringe at the bitterness in his voice.

"She told me how you had dominated her life. She was afraid to marry you, afraid she'd be lost in . . ."

"Lost! The silly fool! I offered her life! Identity, security, place, position. I offered unwisely. I was young. I misread my mark."

Julia knew that his words bore a deep and potent insult. She smarted under the hurt and the hidden challenge.

"Even then," she said softly, "you didn't know much about love."

He drew back as though she had struck him.

"Well, I'll give you one thing. You're not as much a fool as your mother was."

Julia opened her mouth to reply, but he swept ahead.

"Ah, I know now how right I have been, how my will must triumph!"

He rose. He stood so close that she could hear his breathing, catch the spicy scent of his cologne, hear his wristwatch ticking.

"You'll never marry my son. Do you hear me, never! Your mother will not have this triumph over me."

Julia made one last, valiant attempt.

"This has nothing to do with my mother! No part of her at

122

all."

He reached out; his fingers closed over the flesh of her arm. She could feel the hammering pulse against her skin.

"No part of her? Perhaps you are foolish, Julia. Don't you see, Amelia would have me in the end. Have power over me, through my only son. Have access to my wealth, to my very name. And all through you! So easy, so painless for her."

"But I tell you, she doesn't even know about Alex."

His face was closer now; she could feel his breathing. She could see the flecks of color in his dark eyes.

"Then we'll keep it that way, you and I. Won't we, Julia? We'll break this thing before it's even begun."

He loosened his hold on her arm. His fingers grew gentle. His flesh felt warm as he smoothed the skin he had bruised.

"I'll forget this moment. Pretend that I never saw you."

The cold eyes passed over her face; she could feel them caress her.

"You remind me so much of how beautiful she was."

He stood there a moment longer. His eyes consumed her. She trembled beneath the feel of his hand on her arm. At length his fingers trailed down till they reached her wrist, rested there a moment, then dropped.

"You've no part in my life, girl. No part at all. I never want to set eyes on you again."

Julia was fascinated, entranced by the pain in his words, by the emotions she could feel but not understand.

"Leave me."

The words were a hiss, not the usual command.

"Leave me," he repeated.

Julia dropped her eyes, turned, and somehow walked the length of the room. She didn't remember whether the door had been shut or opened. She found herself in the main hall, then clutching the stair rail, feeling hot and chilled, and trembling all over. Someone brushed past her on the stairs; Julia called after. Maria turned with reluctance, her eyes low and veiled.

"Alex is due home any minute. Send him to me. Tell him I must see him at once."

Maria nodded very slightly; there was no other response.

"Do you understand?" Julia pressed, her voice nearly shrill now.

"Yes, miss." The words were as veiled as the guarded face.

Julia turned and somehow made it up the stairs, holding back the tears till her own door was closed and secured. She sat on the bed; she couldn't control her shaking, nor the pain that threatened to tear her whole being apart.

In his study Adam Hutton sat silent, unmoving. For one of the few times in his life he was frightened. Frightened and thwarted and drained by awful emotions. He hated emotion! To him all passions, all feelings were weakness: tools whereby others gained power over one's life. He had constructed a careful fortress around his emotions; he was safe, secured. And now, in one brief moment, his defenses lay scattered in devastation at his feet.

He reached into his desk and drew out a small gold key, then inserted it carefully into a cubby-like drawer. Soundlessly the wood moved at his touch. Encased in the velvet-lined space were a few small items. One was a ring that glowed dusky and dim in the absense of light. Another was an old photo. He drew it out. The face, frozen and young, smiled up from the picture. The beautiful features were delicate and sweet. He moved a finger caressingly over the face.

"Curse follows curse, and you have come back to haunt me."

The words were a whisper, the hand holding the photograph trembled.

"My son loves your daughter. What am I to do?"

124

He made a sound far back in his throat, then sat for long moments, not moving, not stirring. At length the fingers replaced the slender picture, slipped it back into the darkness, then shut and locked the drawer and carefully dropped the gold key back into place. The short, compact figure leaned back heavily; the chair scraped protestingly against polished wood. The thick fingers drummed on the desk, hard and insistent.

"After all these years, my dear, do you think to defeat me?"

In the dim silence the words sounded eerie, unreal. Adam Hutton smiled, a smile that was not pleasant.

"I am older now, and wiser, and much, much stronger. You will not defeat me now, Amelia. Not you nor your Julia."

He laughed—a harsh sound, heavy with satisfaction.

"As I told you years ago, you shall live to regret this. Now you, and your daughter, will see that my words were true."

The words were a comfort; they rewove his shattered protection. He sat alone and with patient determination rebuilt his power—the crutch that supported his life.

Maria was in the kitchen when Alex found her.

"Where's Father? And where is Julia? Have you seen her?"

"Your father is in his study."

"Is Julia with him?"

Alex's tone was growing demanding. Maria sighed.

"Miss Julia, I believe, is in her room. Your father, of course, is waiting to see you."

"Well, he shall have to wait a little longer. I'm going upstairs to Julia. And Maria. . ."

He paused and fixed his bright, sharp gaze upon her, commanding like his father's, but so much warmer. So much like the delicate young woman, long since dead, whose pictures Maria had gazed at these many years.

"Under no circumstances do I wish to be disturbed."

He turned and was gone. She watched his departing figure. Then, shaking her head, she returned to her work. It was not a good sign. It was not a good sign at all. A year ago, or less, he'd have gone in to his father. But now he was on his way up to that girl. And now, no matter what, there would be trouble.

Maria muttered to herself as she did her work. *Dios Mio!* This kind of trouble would not be good!

Julia didn't hear the door as it opened softly. Her first awareness was the touch of Alex's hand on her arm. She started and turned. His face looked pale and troubled. She didn't know that her own looked deathly white.

"Julia, what are you doing?"

"I'm packing, Alex. And when I'm done, will you please drive me to the airport? Or the bus station. Or anywhere. And I want you! I don't want that stiff-necked mute chauffeur."

Good heavens, he couldn't help thinking, *she's beautiful now.*

He took her arm and urged her across the room, then into a rose velvet chair by the wide curtained windows. A breeze brushed past the windows and lifted her hair. Alex felt a terrible aching in his throat.

"Now, tell me about it, Julia. Was Father quite nasty? I was afraid things wouldn't go well with you two alone."

"Oh, Alex, you're far too kind and so awfully naive."

"What do you mean? Control yourself, Julia. It can't have been . . ."

"Well, it was! And this is the end, Alex. Really the end."

He took her hand and smoothed it, brushed back her hair,

and did little things to calm her. Then in a moment or two he tried again.

"Now, tell me about it, Julia. If you can."

She took a deep breath and told him from the beginning.

So far, so good, he thought as he listened to her. *Just as I had expected.* He pressed her hand.

"Julia, there's nothing you and I can't overcome together."

She stared at him, and her eyes grew wide and awful.

"I haven't even begun yet, Alex," she said. "And neither has he. Neither has your father."

She began to unfold the incredible story for him—unlikely, romantic. Julia's mother and his father! He couldn't believe it! A girl much like Julia, innocent, sweet. And his stodgy old father. Had he ever been young and romantic? Dark and handsome? He tried to picture the two. But always his mind came back to himself and Julia. Could this be part of what drew them to each other? Some genetic attraction, inherited, fated between them? It fascinated his mind. He unconsciously smiled.

"Alex, stop it! Why can't you understand what's happening? You think with time and reason things will always come right in the end. Well, we've run out of both—time and reason. Alex, he means it. He'll never allow us to . . ."

"Julia!" He took her face in his hands and kissed her gently. Tears gathered in her eyes, and she blinked them back.

"He's got these crazy ideas about my mother. As if the two of us were not enough! Now he's determined she'll never triumph over him."

Alex felt a cold sensation crawl over his skin. He drew Julia close and cradled her head on his shoulder.

"You finish packing. And then try to rest awhile. I'll go down and . . ."

"Alex, I'm afraid. I'm afraid if you leave, I'll never see you

127

again."

He could read how real the fear was in her eyes. The cold sensation settled more heavily on him.

"If you can't trust me, now is the time to find out," he told her.

His eyes were dark and determined. Julia took a deep breath and gazed at the beautiful eyes. It calmed her a little.

"I trust you," she said. "I just wish . . . oh, Alex, I'm sorry. How can our love cause such wretchedness and pain? I don't want our love to come between you and your father!"

She was in his arms now. He never had loved her more. He tried to explain, to say things too deep for saying. To assure her of the beauty and purity of their love.

"Anything worth having is worth fighting for," he whispered. "So send me off to the battle with one last kiss."

She softly complied, and he left her bravely smiling. As soon as he was out of the room, she dropped to her knees. Alex took the stairs at almost a run.

"It isn't our love that's causing the trouble," he muttered, "it's Father's determined selfishness and pride."

O, that our fathers would applaud our loves,
To seal our happiness with their consents!
O heavenly Julia!
SHAKESPEARE

── 10

Adam Hutton didn't look up as Alex entered. He was signing a stack of papers on his desk. The scratch of his pen was the only sound in the otherwise heavily silent room. Alex stood for a moment watching his father, straining for some kind of clue to his mood and mind. Finally he crossed the room and stood before him.

"I'm busy now, Alex. You'll have to excuse me." Adam still refused to look up.

"I'm afraid not, Father. I've no time to play your games. I'll be leaving soon. If you want to talk to me, it'll have to be now."

Adam screwed on the lid of his pen and laid it down and carefully turned his eyes on his son.

"I take it you've spoken with Julia?"

Alex nodded.

"I hope her woman's tears and entreaties don't blind you, Alex. If you've talked with her, then you know what my feelings are. I have stated my position. I have no intentions . . ."

"Father. You need to know my feelings, don't you think?"

"No, Alex." The reply came swiftly, the voice grew harder. "I'm not interested in your feelings at this point. My interest is in what's right for your future."

"I will decide my future, Father. Not you."

"Don't talk like an absurd young fool, Alex. Don't you know yet you have no future without me?"

"Meaning what?"

Alex had learned by now that his father loved to indulge in wild, general intimidation. But he hedged every time Alex started to pin him down.

"Meaning what?" he repeated.

Adam laughed uncomfortably. "Really, Alex, do I need to spell it out?"

"Yes, Father. I'd like to know just what you're threatening."

Adam's face grew dark and angry, his deep brow creased.

"You're acting the fool, Alex. I didn't expect this. Ever since you went to Utah you've been changed. It's as though you can't see things clearly any more, as though you're purposefully trying to destroy everything we've been building."

A twinge of compassion pricked Alex's heart.

"Dad, it's not that. I've tried so hard to explain. The changes aren't bad if you'd just accept them. I can still be your son and a Mormon. I can still . . ."

"No, you can't! You're blinding yourself to reality, Alex."

Alex paused and stood back on his heels, regarding his father.

"Father, you're sidestepping my question. It's senseless. We could argue this way for hours and not accomplish a thing."

"That's right. So you might as well save us both time and trouble. You might as well realize, Alex, that . . ."

"Father. Stop right now. You may as well know what's going to happen. I'm going back to Salt Lake, and I'm marrying Julia, as soon as the arrangements can be made."

Adam shook his head and snorted—a deep, derisive sound.

"I wouldn't try that if I were you, Alexander. She's poison for you, can't you see that?"

"I'm not 'trying anything,' Father. That's what I shall do. Marry Julia and run the plant and continue . . ."

"As though nothing has happened! With everything just your way!"

Adam was on his feet now, his face dark and angry, the hard lines drawn across the bones of his cheeks.

"What if there isn't a plant anymore, my laddie? No check from Father, no car, no bank account?"

He glared at his son, his breath coming hard and uneven.

"If you're threatening to replace me, Father, go right ahead. You've seen the numbers since I've taken over the plant."

Alex's voice was level, but his eyes were on fire.

"If you can afford to fire me, then do it! Father, I've inherited more than your money from you, you know."

The expression on Alex's face was almost a smile, a look so confident that Adam smouldered.

"I've inherited your skill and your business sense. Your ability to work, your way with men."

Adam made an angry sound far back in his throat. Alex paused. He cocked his head.

"Shall I go on, Father? I can make my own way. I don't need to depend on you."

He paused, and his next words came softer, touched now with emotion.

"I'd rather depend on you, of course. I thought we needed each other, Father. I'd rather be part of you . . . I wish you would . . ."

"Alex! It's my way or no way at all."

Alex rocked on his heels and clapped his hands behind his

back, a little too tightly. His voice sounded tight as he spoke, tight and controlled.

"All right. I'm sorry. More sorry than you know. I . . ."

He hesitated, feeling a sudden sadness within him.

"I don't know quite where to go from here, Father. You'll have to let me know your plans. I'll keep on at the plant till you send someone to replace me. Let me know about everything else—whatever you decide."

He turned and walked a few paces away. Adam stood like a statue but breathed as though he had just run a race. Alex paused but did not turn back.

"I'll send you the date of the wedding. Just in case . . . well . . ."

"For heaven's sake, Alex, what madness is this between us? Stop now, while you can!"

Alex turned slowly around and faced his father. Now there was only sadness in his eyes. He could read nothing in his father's face and eyes beyond the seething anger that seemed to consume them.

"A man has to be true to himself, Father. I don't know what else to do."

"You think because I love you I'll give way. Rant and rave awhile and then give in to you!"

Adam was nearly shouting, his voice uncontrolled and unsteady.

Alex studied the man before him, trying to penetrate beyond the bluff, beyond the hard and angry exterior. But he couldn't find a way inside. With a lonely shudder, he gave up the effort. Adam still glared at him, waiting for him to speak.

"You do what you have to do, Father."

The words were softly, carefully spoken. Alex turned and walked away and out of the room.

For long minutes Adam struggled for control, torn by

emotions he didn't want to feel, hurt and exposed, and angry that he was hurting, aware how closely his weaknesses matched his strength.

"He bullied me into letting him join the Mormons. He thinks I'll give in again. I know he does."

He was trembling still; he couldn't stop the trembling.

"But this time I'll teach the puppy a lesson!"

He made his way to his desk, refusing to think, to temper his impulse in any way. He thumbed through a black directory, found a number, dialed it, his fingers shaking and impatient. Two rings, three. He drummed his hand on the desk top. A click and at last a voice on the other end.

"General Gordon's office. May I help you?" a woman's voice answered.

"Tell Lewis this is Adam Hutton calling. Tell him it's urgent I speak with him at once."

"One moment, sir."

The voice was more respectful. Adam grimaced unconsciously as he held the line. Maybe Alex would learn a little respect this time.

*   *   *   *   *   *

It was a long time before either Alex or Julia talked of that night: of their hurried leave-taking, of the lonely journey home, of the feelings of failure and sorrow. Julia urged Alex to postpone the wedding and give his father some time, but Alex refused. She knew in her heart he was right; she knew Adam Hutton would never give in or change. She went ahead with their plans, but her heart was aching. And she had some dark moments of her own yet to face. She had to tell her own father and mother.

It was past nine o'clock on Wednesday night of the week

after their return. The telephone rang. Vera came into Julia's room, her face uncertain.

"Long distance. I think it's your mother," she said.

Julia walked to the phone, her mind in an instant turmoil, wondering what in the world she was going to say.

"Julia, are you all right? We've been worried about you. You haven't written in such a long time."

Julia was surprised at how homesick the sound of that voice could make her!

"I'm sorry, Mother. I'm sorry you had to call. But it's so wonderful to hear your voice again."

They talked for awhile; she told Julia news of the family.

"Did you know that Marc has been sent into action?" she asked. Julia felt a strange constriction at her throat.

"No, no. He hasn't written for quite some time."

The direction of the conversation was becoming a little uncomfortable.

"Mother." Julia hesitated. Now was the moment. "I've something important to tell you, but it may take some time. If you'd rather, I'll just write you a nice long letter about it."

"No." Her mother's voice sounded strong and certain. "No, Julia, you tell me all about it now."

It wasn't too bad at the first. Julia told things in order, trying to create a tenderness for Alex before—before she had to tell the rest. Her mother listened, with very few reactions. How Julia wished she could see her face and know what she felt!

When she came to the part about Adam, she had some trouble. And after she'd stumbled through it, her mother was silent so long that she felt a sensation of panic rising inside her. As it was, she had toned things down an awfully lot, especially Adam's fanatical opposition. When her mother's words came at last, they were unexpected.

"Julia, you mustn't do this. Do you hear me?"

"I hear you, but I have no idea what you mean."

"I mean Adam was right—this thing is no good between you. You can't marry this boy and expect things to turn out right."

"Mother! Haven't you listened to what I've been saying? Alex is everything wonderful you could imagine. I love him; I trust him. I . . ."

"Julia, honey, you've lost your perspective. And you haven't known him long enough to be sure. You want to start out like this, with everything against you?"

Julia nearly broke then, the tears made her voice unsteady.

"Mother, I know this is what I'm supposed to do."

"Yes, and what if the boy turns out to be like his father? Hard and didactic. What if he turns against you?"

"Mother!"

"Well, even if he doesn't you'd be part of the *family*. Nothing good can come from that association. This is what comes from betraying your own kind, Julia."

She could hear the sadness her mother was struggling to conceal. She felt so helpless.

"Oh, Mother, please, please try to understand."

"Understand? You want to marry this boy—a Mormon. A Mormon like you, who's turned against his own family. Marry him in a . . . a . . . what do you call it—temple? Where your father and I can't even come. What then, Julia? What kind of a life can you make together? What can you hope to build from a mess like that?"

Julia didn't answer; she couldn't. She was crying, holding the phone so her mother wouldn't hear. At last she got out the words.

"I love you, Mother. So much. So much. I wish you knew."

She wasn't sure her mother even heard her.

"Well, you've surely turned my world topsy-turvy. What a surprise to drop in your mother's lap. Whoever would have thought such a thing could happen?"

She paused. Julia could almost hear her thinking.

"Listen, Julia." Her voice was still confident and persuasive. "Don't go ahead with this. I'm warning you, if you do, you'll be sorry. You'll come crying home to us, with your life in ruins. You mark my words, you . . ."

"Mother! Mother, stop it!"

Mercifully, there was silence on the other end. Julia struggled to continue.

"Mother, listen. I'm marrying Alex, and nothing can change my mind. I guess . . ."

She had to stop for a minute, bite her lip, swallow back the tears.

"I pray that with time you'll see and understand. Until then, Mother, please . . . please don't stop loving me."

There was silence still, except for Julia's soft crying. At last she heard a voice, very soft, very low.

"Julia, please forget it. Please . . . just come home."

"Oh, Mother, don't!" Julia thought her heart would break. "I can't. I . . . I'll write. Please trust me. Mother, I love you . . . I love you. Give my love to Laura and my special love to Daddy."

She replaced the phone, the pain like a fire inside her, blotting out all thought, all other feeling. She went to her room and stretched out across the bed. But the tears wouldn't come, tears that might offer relief now.

She stared out her window, unseeing, one thought in her head, that screamed itself over and over, through the pain: I love Alex! I love him. I love him.

136

Actually, a temple marriage took very little planning, especially in wartime, especially with no large families, no fanfare and big celebrations to prepare. They set a date, and the days moved quickly forward. Alex wrote to his father; Julia wrote her promised letter, with a special note to the father she adored. And with each day one thing became more certain—their love, their total trust in one another.

Temporarily Julia had forgotten all about Nolan. One evening he appeared at Vera's door.

"It's rude to look quite so shocked, my darling. Although I know I deserve it."

Nolan laughed. The bright laugh that was Nolan.

He chose Vera's best chair and made himself comfortable. Julia found herself still awkwardly standing. And she realized Nolan was staring at her.

"My gad, you look good to me, Julia."

She perched on the edge of a chair, uncomfortable still.

"You cheeks look flushed. Don't tell me you're embarrassed. I guess I'd better come around more often. Has it been that long since I teased you, Julia?"

She returned his smile. "I meant to call you, Nolan. Last week after . . ."

"Oh, yes, well, I should have called again myself. Serves me right—expecting you to be instantly available, just 'cause I had the fancy to see you."

Nolan! Why in the world must he be so charming? This is going to be hard, Julia thought to herself.

"Nolan, get serious a minute. I've something to tell you."

"You ran away and got married over the weekend. Just to spite me for waiting so long to call."

When Julia didn't smile, Nolan hesitated.

"Come on now, out with it, Julia," he urged.

"That's not a bad guess," she said. "I have met someone. It

. . . it's happened awfully quickly . . ."

"Aw, come on now, Julia, not with you, my conservative girl from Freeport."

"Nolan, please stop teasing. Just long enough to listen."

He sat back in his chair then, his warm eyes resting on her, flexing his hands together as he listened. He let her finish without interruptions, though he shook his head in amazement a time or two.

"I thought I was a mover," he said. "I can't believe it."

Julia dropped her eyes; his gaze was so penetrating.

"Well, it sounds like the real thing, Julia."

He rose like a disturbed cat springing and unconsciously paced back and forth across the room.

"It's hard to believe. My gad, it's just hard to believe this."

He paused, and his eyes grew reflective and kinder now.

"You sure know how to walk into trouble, honey. You—and you're not the type for it at all."

"I know. And remember, I've got no one but you to thank for it."

He looked chagrined, perhaps even a little dismayed.

"I know, I know. I have nightmares already," he protested.

She smiled. "Oh, Nolan, it is strange how things have turned out. So totally unexpected, so . . ."

"Yes, I know it."

His voice sounded glum and not in a put-on way.

"Well, it is my own fault, entirely. I should never have left you at loose ends so long. I've got no one to blame but myself."

His blue eyes looked unhappy. Julia hated to see the blue eyes with no sparkle in them.

"He can make you happy? Are you sure about that, Julia?"

He stopped his pacing and stood very close beside her. "That's important, you know, especially with so much against you."

"I'm sure, Nolan. Totally peaceful and happy and sure."

The blue eyes gazed into hers a moment longer.

"Well, what more can I say? Except, be happy, Julia."

He took her hand, and the blue eyes looked bright and misty.

"I do want you to be happy, Julia, you know. That was my impulse for getting you into all this in the first place."

"I know." She leaned and kissed his tanned cheek gently. "I shall always remember and be grateful and . . . and love you for it, Nolan."

He nodded, the blue eyes searching her face, very warm and affectionate.

"Well, that's more than I deserve."

The smile was lopsided, very strained. Julia felt her own eyes moist and teary now.

"I'll still be here, you know. I won't just walk out of your life. If you ever need anything, anybody . . ."

Julia nodded. "I know that. You wouldn't have even had to say it."

She walked him to the door. He still held her hand.

"You're a rare and beautiful girl, my little Julia. I'm very glad I was in Chicago that crazy night."

He released her hand but leaned over and kissed her gently, his lips tender and silken against her own. Then he turned, lithe and graceful, and walked away—not pausing or calling back with a jaunty quip or two.

Julia, watching, knew he was walking out of her life and ending yet another phase. How she hated endings! Even though they brought beginnings in their wake. There seemed always pain and loss and parting before a new sun could break through and shine.

She sighed. This was the last ending of her girlhood. The

next beginning would mark her a woman and wife, bringing more change than she had thought or dreamed of.

Must we part? — Ay, hand from hand,
my love, and heart from heart.
SHAKESPEARE

11

Julia had daydreamed about getting married since she was little. The lacy white dress, the long trailing veil, the solemn organ, the walk down the aisle—with everyone watching and weeping a little. This was nothing at all like her dreams. This was totally new. Totally personal, totally solemn and sacred.

At first she felt overwhelmed and a little uncertain. But Vera was there to take her through each step. And before she knew it she stood in the sealing room with Alex, then knelt across from him, listening to the words that sealed them as man and wife for eternity.

She could feel the light and joy flow through and around her. She saw it when she looked into Alex's eyes. She could feel power and the sweetest sensation of peace. And love, touching every person in the room—part of the purity, part of the warmth and light.

After leaving the temple, the feeling still clung about them, the glow remained in their faces and their eyes. The reception Vera and Celia had planned was lovely. Julia didn't feel they knew many people and hadn't expected a crowd. But she hadn't reckoned on the people who worked for Alex who came in numbers, as well as friends from their wards. On and on streamed the names and the faces. But as long as Alex was beside her, it didn't matter. She could have stood beside him the whole night through.

Some time in the evening Nolan appeared. Julia didn't see him until he was right before her. With a flush on her face she introduced him to Alex. The two men looked at each other carefully. Then Alex smiled.

"I owe you, Nolan Hart. The kind of debt beyond repaying."

Nolan nodded. His grin was wide, his blue eyes sparkling.

"I won't argue with you there. Just so long as you know. Just as long as you appreciate what you've got here."

He leaned over and kissed Julia's cheek and murmured in passing.

"He'll do all right. Trust you to know how to pick them."

"After all, I found you, didn't I?" she replied.

He shook his head at that. "Julia, Julia, I'm going to miss you."

He squeezed her thin, gloved hand, then passed along the line and out of sight.

There was only a time or two when she thought of her parents, and a little strain of sorrow swept through her joy. Yet she knew she couldn't share this happiness with them. It was something they weren't prepared to understand. She would have to be patient and hope and plan for the future. And meanwhile she had today, and Alex. And who could be unhappy in face of that?

At last they found themselves alone, in the quiet apartment they had furnished and fixed together. It was as if all the gathered joy of the evening still clung about them, the laughter and the love, the warmth of good wishes, the support of so many people who cared.

And beyond that, and through that, the shining golden moment when their souls had merged with eternity into one. And now the last expression, the last coming together, much sweeter than Julia had ever thought it could be. In every way they belonged to one another, and the joy between them filled up the little room and spilled out into the night and sang in the stillness; it was part of the endless melody of life that very few mortals are lucky enough to hear . . . and fewer still to sing with their own voices.

*   *   *   *   *   *

The next few days passed much like a quiet dream. They learned each other, adjusted to different ways, did little happy things to fill the hours, aware of the beauty and sweetness of every moment.

They almost held their breaths, but nothing happened. No word from California, no ripples, no swells to disturb the smooth perfection of this time. Alex went back to the plant and the days continued. No phone calls, no official envelopes in the mail. They began to relax but only a little. Julia felt part of a game of cat and mouse—at the mercy of the big claw when it closed down. Until Adam chose to strike, what could they do but hope and pray and love each other.

Julia quit her job at *Utah Ice and Storage* and went to work with Alex instead. It was his idea; in fact, he nearly insisted.

"You're twice as qualified as any girl we've got there. Besides, I want you to learn the business. I want the men to get to know you."

"You want to keep your eye on me," she teased.

"Now where did you get such a crazy idea?"

They laughed in each other's arms, and the matter was settled.

They were always together; and each new day was better than the last. They fell into an easy, gentle pattern which included Sunday dinners at Vera's house, and mountain drives with the top down on the Packard, and walks on Temple Square when the day had cooled. Julia liked the people Alex worked with, especially the big, quiet foreman, Oscar Clayton. She liked the respect in his voice when he talked to Alex. She liked the warm, honest look in his eyes. Julia wrote her parents long, loving letters, trying to make them see how happy she was. Alex sent off his weekly reports and kept things humming. August days slipped gently into September. And one bright September morning the claw came down.

Alex was alone when he got the letter. He knew immediately everything it meant. Official! There wasn't a thing he could do about it. The U. S. Government; it was out of his hands. With fingers cold as ice he tore at the paper. Official notice of induction. United States Army. Induction date: September 10. His father and General Gordon. Alex swore softly. Something he hadn't done in a long, long time.

He told his secretary to hold all calls and informed her that he wanted no interruptions.

"And that includes Julia," he said, trying to smile.

He locked his office and dialed California. He felt sick inside; he had never felt this way before. His father picked up the phone.

"Why, Alex, how are you? What's that you say? Came in the mail today? Well, yes, it took Lewis longer than I expected. Some red tape about you living in Utah, not in his state of jurisdiction, you know."

"This is lower than anything I expected, Father. Of all the things you could choose to do . . ."

"This was one that I thought might get your attention."

The laugh that followed was short and harsh.

"Seems it's done the trick. Now, listen Alex, I've a replacement on his way there now. Should arrive by tomorrow afternoon. Fellow by the name of Clarence Johnson. Been in the organization a long time. A little on the dull side, but . . ."

"Father, stop it. What about Julia? What about my wife?"

"Oh, yes. When you leave, Alex, Julia goes with you. Unless you want her to go through the embarrassment of being fired by the new man. But I don't think . . ."

"You've been very thorough, Father. Congratulations."

The sick feeling rose like bile in Alex's throat.

"What happens to Julia when I walk out the door?"

"Hell, Alex, that's your problem, not mine. I told you not to marry the girl."

"And you're sending me to California for training. Why not one of the sites in Utah? You know there are more. . ."

"That's right. I know there are places near you. Lewis did a good job, didn't he? Wants you under his wing, I think that's how he put it. A clean cut, Alex—clean break with Utah. You're lucky, boy, to rate personal attention from General Gordon. There aren't many . . ."

"All right, Father. All right, I get the point."

Alex struggled to know what to do, what to say now. He had never felt such coldness from his father before.

"Five days. You haven't given me much warning."

"This is wartime, Alex. Remember? Funny how that hasn't bothered you much till now."

Alex felt a ringing in his head and a dull ache beginning behind his eyes.

"Father, I don't think you realize what you're doing."

"Time to take your medicine, Alex. Not much you can do about it now."

Adam's voice smacked with satisfaction. Alex felt his stomach turn as he listened.

"Nor you, Father. It's out of your hands, too. I hope to heaven you don't live to regret it."

Alex put down the phone. His hands were shaking. It was all he could do to grasp what was happening. His mind was churning round in circles. How could he ever bear to tell Julia? See the pain leap into her beautiful eyes? How could he walk away and leave her, when he had promised to love and care for her all his life?

Suddenly that life had changed its meaning, become just another leaf in an ugly whirlpool that sucked up thousands of lives and tore them to pieces, scattering them on the winds of today, with nothing left for tomorrow, nothing but memory. What did he have to offer Julia now?

Adam sat in his office, alone in the silence. *Damn the boy! His voice had sounded so sad. Time Alex grew up—best thing that could happen to him.*

He stomped out of the room and yelled for his secretary, rattling off a list of instructions as long as his arm. Then he stalked through the offices, growling and criticizing. He couldn't get Alex's words out of his mind: *I hope to heaven you don't live to regret it.* Already he could feel a cold fear growing inside him; already he wished things he wasn't ready yet to admit or recognize.

Julia sat and listened, but something was frozen inside her. Her eyes were dry, though her face was very pale.

"You see, it's Father's influence that's kept me out this long," Alex was saying. "With his involvement in a few priority industries it wasn't too hard. And then, of course, his relationship with General Gordon."

Julia nodded, not trusting herself to speak, wondering if her words would sound hollow—hollow and empty like she was feeling inside.

"Gordon. Isn't that the name of the girl you were supposed to marry?"

"Lillie Gordon. Lewis's only daughter. Her mother died when she was thirteen. By that time it was long established that we would marry. But after Meg Gordon's death, the two old men . . . well, they tied the knots even tighter than before."

"That would be only natural," Julia murmured, though a prick of some feeling she couldn't identify touched her. Jealousy? Fear? She couldn't be sure.

"In the beginning I wanted to go," Alex continued. "I was younger—I thought it was right to serve my country. It's not that I'm not patriotic anymore. It's just, well . . ."

He smiled, with tender, boyish appeal.

"I guess you could say I've changed my allegiance a little."

They talked long into the night; there was so much to settle and so very little time. Alex made arrangements to transfer all funds, all stocks and bonds in his name to Julia, only to discover that they had been frozen—that Adam had beat them there, as in everything. Everything Alex had was tied up with his father, with the huge corporation, in a dozen legal ways. He had never felt a need for complete independence. And now, of course, there wasn't time.

"Your service pay will suffice," Julia assured him. "I'll get another job if I have to. Better than sitting around missing you. It won't take much for me to get by, Alex."

It wasn't the money Julia was worried about. War and hunger and disease—Alex suffering. She couldn't bear to send him away to that! Death? She refused to allow death to enter the picture. Fate wouldn't have gone to such trouble to bring them together, only to snatch him away and end it all. She believed they were meant to live and have children and accomplish things for a lifetime. That belief was her only salvation now.

Alex planned a surprise for their last night together. They drove in the Packard out to Saltair, along the white salt-desert to where the Moorish castle rose on its thousands of pilings, garish and grand. There they walked and explored and reminisced together, danced on the polished wood floor, and stood in the silence to watch the sunset in splendor all about them.

The sky was on fire, the mountains, the distant shore—every hue of blue and lavender, gold, and crimson. The sunset was part of the promise they both had felt, the eternal beauty and wonder of their love.

The sunset died, but the beauty between them lingered. Later, as darkness settled, a wind blew up. At first they thought to leave, but hesitated, loathe to end the magic of this last night. The wind increased, whipping caverns into the water, salty spray across startled strollers; and still the wind grew stronger. Some, alarmed, stood watching the heaving waters. Others laughed even more gaily, ignoring the storm. The thousands of lights winked and trembled . . . and then there was darkness, and gasps rose up from hundreds of voices together.

Then one long, steady beam threw its light across the shadows; the beacon on the front of the train. It was enough. The band whipped up their music, people poured onto the dance floor, their shadows leaping and trembling before them. In the glow of that single light the evening continued, the music and fun and bravado of youth and love.

It was part of their own special magic for Alex and Julia. Whatever the spell was that drew them at first together, they felt it now. They had found each other, and nothing else could matter.

Long into the night they danced in each other's arms. And later, much later, they lay in the stillness together, flesh against flesh, heart against beating heart. They had pushed their fears away, and for these few hours nothing could mar the perfection of their love, the joy and faith that sang between their spirits. Their love was strong enough to weather tomorrow—whatever evils Tomorrow held in its hands. They knew that and were comforted by the knowledge, as their last moments together burned brightly . . . flickered . . . then died.

* * * * * *

Six weeks. Six hard, lonely weeks. Yet they had passed quickly. Much more quickly than Julia had expected them to. She had passed another birthday, another milestone. One year older and one whole year in the Church. And she'd thought things had been rough the year before! What if someone had told her about today? Of the love and joy, of the terrible pain?

Alex wrote, but Alex was very busy, training day and night, working, preparing. *It would help,* she thought glumly, *if I had more to do.* Her days, so full of love and excitement and wonder, had become suddenly empty—empty and dull and grey. There was no one and nothing to fill the empty hours. Vera had taken not one, but two new boarders. This was still wartime, and money was very dear. But Julia felt a little out of place there, especially now that Alex was no longer with her. So she didn't drop in to visit as much as before.

She had swallowed her pride and gone back to *Utah Ice and Storage.* They had been very kind and very apologetic; they would love to have her back, but there were no openings. Alex's first service check had arrived. It was a decent amount, but it wouldn't be enough. Not to maintain her current living arrangements. She thought seriously about getting a smaller apartment, something more modest. She spent days searching for a job. She needed money now, and she needed to save it, because she wasn't sure; she didn't know what to expect.

Six weeks; she was almost sure now that she was pregnant. She hadn't been to see a doctor yet; she'd wait just awhile longer. But so many signs were there. It must be true. Though it seemed impossible and a little unfair. How could she live through that kind of a thing alone? And yet, she wouldn't be alone, would she? If there was a baby, some miracle that was part of both Alex and her, then she'd never be really alone again.

So she fought the loneliness and the queasy feelings, searched for work, and tried not to count the days. Nine weeks passed. She asked a neighbor, a stranger, to recommend a good doctor. She went there alone. Dr. Stevens was LDS; he was older and kindly, with a patient sort of fatherly air.

"You're pregnant, all right," he said, patting her shoulder. "There's a baby in there. What do you think about that?"

Julia didn't know what to think. She felt warm and excited, as though she held some incredible secret in her hands. She listened carefully to the doctor's instructions, determined to do everything just right. Hearing the words pronounced out loud made this unknown baby seem suddenly a hundred times more alive and real.

She walked out of the office and slid into the Packard; she couldn't help smiling, though she felt rather silly. *I ought to look different,* she thought. *People ought to notice. I must look different; there must be some way to tell.*

She felt so different, so special, so bubbling over. She had to *tell* someone! She drove the car toward Vera's. Everybody else would be working now. What about Alex? How was she going to tell him? She wouldn't even be able to watch his face when he heard!

She pulled up in Vera's driveway and rang the doorbell, again and again, but no one came to the door. She must be out shopping. A wave of discouragement swept over Julia. She shook it off. *That's nonsense,* she told herself. *I won't allow it.*

She drove home to the apartment and fixed herself a salad, then wrote in her journal and went for a little walk. But every hour dragged longer than the last one. By evening she felt very lonely and very lost and very much like crying. She went to bed early and made up lovely dreams about the baby: what it would be and what it would look like, what they ought to name it, what clothes she would buy, how her mother and father would act when they saw their first grandchild, what Alex would do when she laid his child in his arms. Little innocent dreams laced with longing, dreams that kept her tossing and turning all night.

Four days passed. It was Sunday. The telephone rang. Long distance. Alex's voice came over the wire, sounding a little muffled and far away. But Alex, very much Alex! Julia was trembling.

"Why are you calling? Is everything all right?"

He assured her it was. He told her little things about training, interesting things to pass the time.

"What have you been doing to keep yourself busy," he teased her, "while I've been working myself to the bone down here?"

Her heart gave a little lurch.

"Well, actually, I've been doing a thing or two you might not have expected."

She tried to keep the excitement out of her voice.

"Whatever does that mean?" He sounded a little worried. "Are *you* all right?"

"All right, yes." She hesitated. "But not 'the same.' You might say I'm a little different."

"Julia?" He sounded confused and very uncertain.

"Well, you see, I've been getting sick every morning. And last week I went to the doctor and . . ."

"Oh, my heavens, Julia! Are you trying to tell me you're going to have a baby?"

His voice had grown loud and excited. Julia smiled as she listened.

"That's right! Alex, can you believe it? The doctor said May—the end of May."

Alex laughed, a rich, happy laugh that sent gladness through her. Then he spent five precious minutes asking her questions. What had the doctor told her? What should she do? How was she feeling? She must take care of herself.

She drank in his love, like a person parched and thirsting. But finally, somewhere, the minutes had to end. They had to say good-bye.

"Do you know when you're leaving? Do you have a date yet?"

Alex hesitated. "No. No, but I'll know soon. And I'll call you again. Oh, Julia . . ."

They said good-bye half a dozen times, and each time grew harder. At last Julia hung up the phone. The line went dead. Alex held the cold, buzzing instrument for minutes before he roused himself and hung it back again.

Thank heaven I asked her first what she was doing! What if I'd

152

bungled ahead and told her? Julia, Julia!

He walked out into the mild afternoon. He felt so helpless! He had called her to say he was leaving the following Wednesday, a week and a half early, as part of the "general's training." But how could he have told her and spoiled that moment, destroyed her joy and dampened the miracle? Besides, just maybe he wouldn't be leaving on Wednesday. Just maybe he could persuade the general now . . .

"Come in, Alex. It's hot out there for November. But then, it will be a great deal hotter where we're going, eh, son?"

The general leaned back in his chair, relaxed and congenial.

"What can I do for you, Alex?"

Alex explained, presenting his case as persuasively as he could. The general frowned, then started drumming his fingers. Alex knew the man he was talking to well. Before he was even through speaking, he knew he had lost.

"Well, I'm sorry, Alex. I wish I'd known this sooner. But the girl's all right? No problems or anything?"

Alex shook his head.

"Well, you're lucky there, and I'm sorry about the other. A pass would be a beastly thing to arrange—for that far away. This close to date of departure."

He shook his head, his handsome face drawn into lines of "official concern."

"Now, I could arrange a postponement of your departure. But what good would that do? Wouldn't help the girl. And it wouldn't help you either, Alex."

He fixed his innocent, scrutinizing gaze on the boy.

"I've been counting on you, Alex."

"Yes, I know, sir."

"Part of the team. I need your kind of men. Sharp and

dependable."

He leaned back in his chair; comfortable, in control again.

"And face it, Alex. Part of the general's cortege. There are privileges not every . . ."

"I understand, sir. And I appreciate all you've done."

"I know that, Alex. And you know that I'm glad to have you."

Alex leaned forward and shook the older man's hand. Then he straightened, saluted smartly, and left the room, feeling defeated and tired and old inside.

Adam scowled, and the scowl grew deeper the longer he listened.

"Is it anything to be worried about, do you think?"

"No, no," his old friend assured him, "just thought I'd inform you. Have you heard from the boy yourself?"

"No, he doesn't call. Still smarting." Adam snorted. "Proud, like his father."

Both men laughed, in understanding of one another.

"Listen, Lewis, Alex may not have told things quite as they are. This girl is young and high-strung like her mother. I suspect there may be," he paused, "some problems brewing."

"I wondered if that might not be the case."

"Yes, well, I'm not even sure where she's living right now. There are rumbles of 'going home to Mama,' you know."

Adam sighed, managing to sound both concerned and tired.

"Lewis, you'd better send everything of Alex's here to me. Everything official that comes through your office. Then I'll just have to sort things out the best I can."

"Will do. Well, that's settled. Looks like we're off to the Pacific now." The eagerness was plain in the general's voice.

154

"Next time you see that boy of yours, Adam, he'll be a man!"

"Thanks to you, Lewis."

"My pleasure, my pleasure, Adam. He's a wonderful boy, Adam, wonderful boy."

Adam hung up the phone feeling satisfied. He could trust his old friend implicitly, he knew. Time was on his side. He had learned to be patient. He could sit back and wait for things to work out his way. Not that he didn't have plans to help things along—now and then, here and there, as he saw the chance arise. But for the first time in weeks he allowed himself to feel hopeful. With time they would all come to see that Adam was right—Alex and Julia and Amelia. Above all, Amelia.

I will remain the loyal'st husband
that did e'er plight troth..
I know him and I love him. —
Till he come home again, I will forbear.
SHAKESPEARE

12

The apartment was awfully tiny and terribly dirty. But the price was right, so it would just have to do. It was also close to the drugstore where she would be working. She had a week to clean and get things ready. Next week, the first of December, she would move in.

Julia drove Alex's sleek, shiny car back to the apartment, the place where their life together had begun, and parked it carefully in the garage at the back of the building. The car, which she always had loved, seemed a link with Alex. The leather smell inside, his gloves in the side pocket, his tools in the back, all reminded her of him.

Thursday was Thanksgiving. Vera had invited her; Celia had begged and pleaded with her to come. She ought to go. It wouldn't be good alone here, lonely and brooding. Their first Thanksgiving . . . not even together. Alex was probably safe in Honolulu by now. Just where he would go from there she wasn't certain. He had assured her when he called to tell of his leaving that being in the general's private party would guarantee that he wasn't anywhere where the action would be too hot. In fact, he had been chafing already at visions of boredom and inaction. He wanted to fly. He had always wanted to fly. He didn't welcome the idea of sitting around eating papayas.

Julia smiled as she remembered the conversation. He had sounded so young and impatient, so much a boy. Well, he was gone now, and she was alone, and it wouldn't help for her to sit around feeling sorry for herself. She dialed Vera's number and told her she'd be there on Thursday, warmed at how sincerely pleased Vera sounded. As she hung up the phone, the doorbell started ringing. *Who could be coming here?* she wondered.

"Aren't you going to invite me in?"

Nolan winked at her boldly and cocked the new army hat so it sat on his head at just the perfect angle. He looked very handsome.

"What are you doing in that uniform?" she asked, not liking the feeling of fear that had come upon her.

"Can't run away forever." He perched on a chair, took off the hat and twirled it around in his hands.

"You're supposed to be impressed by the uniform. Ooh and aah some. That's what the other girls do."

The blue eyes were warm and sparkling. Julia smiled. "I'm a married woman now, remember? But you do look alarmingly handsome, Nolan."

He grinned back and nodded his head in acknowledgment.

"This is a pretty nice set-up you've got here, Julia."

He looked about the apartment appreciatively. Julia dropped her eyes in case he read something in them.

"If you have to be an army widow, this is the way to go."

"Well, you promised you'd be here, and now you're running out, too. First I have too many men and then none at all."

He responded to the banter in her tone. It was better to keep things light and easy between them.

"Aw, you know you'll be glad to be rid of me."

They talked awhile. He told her about his unit—bright, colorful talk that avoided the serious issues. Too soon, Julia felt, he rose to leave.

"I'll be going now. Listen, you take care of yourself, Julia."

He moved until he was standing quite close beside her. The concern in the bright blue eyes was very real.

"It's you who'd better be careful," Julia told him.

"I'll be all right. I lead a charmed life, remember?"

He reached out an arm and suddenly drew her close.

"I mean it, Julia. You're very special to me. Remember that, will you, no matter what?"

She nodded, not trusting herself to speak. And when he drew her closer, she let him kiss her and trembled at his touch. When he drew away, there were tears in the blue eyes, but he doffed his hat and saluted.

After he left, Julia stood at the window a long time, gazing at nothing, torturing herself with thoughts she could not resolve. She moved to sit down on the couch, feeling suddenly faint and a little dizzy and realized that she hadn't told Nolan about the baby. She closed her eyes. *Was there nothing in life secure? Nothing she could hold to that wouldn't change?*

She knew the answer, of course. Truth didn't change. Truth and love. No matter how people suffered, or feared, or questioned, truth was always there. And love . . . to make the suffering bearable.

*　　*　　*　　*　　*　　*

When the huge, four-motored Douglas transport had touched down at Honolulu, Alex had felt keenly how far away from home he was. Five thousand miles from America and Julia, in a world of sun and water and palm trees and tropical fruits. It didn't seem to take long to adjust, though, to the place. Within hours he'd taken a shower, changed into light khaki clothes, and eaten his share of beautiful yellow papaya. Actually, that was the frightening thing. In some ways the war seemed more remote and unreal than it had at the base in California. There was no rationing of anything in Honolulu. And although numbers of uniformed men walked the streets, the soft climate, the warmth, the loveliness left one spellbound, in a feeling of languid stupor that wasn't quite real.

Alex set up house in the officers' quarters. The general, apparently, had an actual house, and a hostess to run it, as well as a native housekeeper and native gardeners and native errand boys. The hostess, Alex guessed, was none other than Lillie, flown over earlier with some of the officers' wives, anxious to greet her father and make him at home; anxious to see Alex again after so much time.

He had learned their destination from the general: The Mariana Islands, an incredible distance off, even from here. Alex studied the Navy slick sheet entitled "Airline Distances in the Pacific" and could understand the irony of what they had printed below: "Our Enemy, Geography." It was thirty-five hundred miles from Pearl Harbor to the Marianas—all over water. But Alex was anxious to go. The one thing he didn't want was too much leisure, too much time to think, to be alone.

It was only two days until Thanksgiving, and the general informed him that he'd leave for the Islands the following day. On Thursday Lillie expected him for dinner. Two o'clock sharp. Alex nodded and saluted and wondered how long these arrangements had been made and how many people were in on the arranging.

She came to him with just the right combination of the gracious hostess and the wounded girlfriend-left-behind.

"Alex, how well you look. A little taller?"

She laid her hand on his shoulder, a moment or two too long, then let her fingers trail down the length of his arm and gave his hand a warm little squeeze. Her perfume was sweet and rich, like the smells of the island, her dress thin and filmy over a shape still lithe and slim. It disturbed Alex to look at her and remember the times he had touched her and held her, the ways he had felt. He could watch her still and appreciate her beauty, but the feelings weren't there anymore. But when she looked at him, her eyes became deep and dreamy. And he knew Lillie well enough to know that for her nothing had changed at all.

There was a group at the general's home; with a group he was safe. As long as he avoided being with her alone he was okay. The food was good, the company genial and friendly. Alex sat in his shirt sleeves and gazed out at the dazzling sun, wondering what the weather was like in Utah. He hoped that Julia was spending the day at Vera's. He hoped she was feeling well and not too lonely. Their first Thanksgiving . . .

"Here, darling. A Bloody Mary is just what you need to weather the afternoon slump."

Lillie perched on the edge of his chair, her thin skirts trailing along the skin of his arm. He took the drink she carried and set it down on the table. She puckered her smooth brow into a pretty frown.

"Daddy was right then. He said you'd given up drinking. How boring, Alex! Whatever for?"

He smiled at her, refusing the baited answer. "Do you like it here in Hawaii?" he asked.

"Yes, I like the sun and the servants and all the parties."

She trailed a finger softly along his chin, following the line of his jaw, then brushing her fingers gently back through his hair.

160

"And, of course, all the handsome uniformed young men."

He drew back ever so slightly, away from her fingers.

"You'll dry up on that awful desert if you're not careful."

She made a face, then laughed, her blue eyes warm. Honey hair, honey skin, and honey laughter.

"But then, you don't look any worse for the wear. And, anyway, Father's rescued you, hasn't he?"

Alex felt a chill prick the hairs at the back of his neck. Lillie had her claws out, all right.

"Lillie, if you really believe the Marianas will be some kind of glorified paradise, you're wrong. And the cockpit of a B-29 bomber could beat any desert for plain old discomfort, I think."

She pouted, and this time sincerely. Little hard specks appeared in the soft blue eyes. She rose and carefully straightened her skirts about her, aware that Alex's eyes were on her still.

"I'm sorry you're so disagreeable, Alex."

She started to float away, then stopped and turned, throwing him a soft glance over her shoulder.

"The Bloody Mary would help, you know."

Alex watched after her, unconsciously clenching and unclenching his hand into a fist. This wasn't going to be pleasant, not one bit. The sooner he got out of here, the better.

*   *   *   *   *   *

Thanksgiving had been a long and miserable day, even though Adam had worked the entire morning. There was still too much time to think, to be alone. He wondered how things were working with Alex and Lillie. He knew how stubborn the boy could be. But then Lillie was pretty persistent and very persuasive. Give him awhile, a few months of that

161

stinking Pacific.

He grimaced as he thumbed through the Utah figures. He'd already been over those pages a dozen times. Once more wouldn't change anything, except maybe his blood pressure. But he fumed at the thought of the money he was losing. What in the world was the matter with Johnson? He'd always done a decent job before. But the figures from Utah kept steadily falling, the reports were sloppy, the details poorly kept. Those Mormons were being perverse, that must be the problem. Refusing to support him because the man wasn't one of them.

Adam knew that wasn't true; he could see the handwriting. But it made him feel better for the moment, anyway. He refused to admit that he needed Alex. And as he wandered about the grounds of the big, empty house, he refused to admit to himself that he was lonely, that, more than anything else, he missed his son.

＊　＊　＊　＊　＊　＊

In Utah Clarence Johnson was very unhappy. He didn't like it here; he didn't like it at all. Heck of a place for a fellow who was social. What did you do for entertainment here? He laughed and poured his third drink of the morning.

That was part of the problem. The boss's son had left everything here humming as smooth as a top. He could straighten out a mess as well as the next guy. But here there was literally nothing to do. The men at the plant were efficient, self-motivated. And every one seemed to let Clarence know that his presence there was extraneous at best. They didn't need him. What's more, they didn't want him. You'd think Alex Hutton had been some kind of a little god. It was freaky, that's what it was, freaky.

His drink was down to ice. He topped it a little. Bad luck

for him that the boy went and got himself drafted. Heck of a place for a fella like him to be stuck. He finished off the drink, but he didn't feel better. Damn war interfered with everybody's life. He'd better watch the bottle, he knew he'd better. The bottle could mess up everything for him. He put the bottle away and cursed things in general: the war and Alex Hutton and the desert and the boredom of this miserable dead-end place.

* * * * * *

At last Julia was settled into the new apartment, though hardly reconciled to the drab, cramped space. The weather was mild for December, and she was grateful. She hardly drove the Packard anymore but walked to work or on bad days took the buses. It was hard to stand at the drugstore counter all day, and the hours dragged. But Julia forced herself to be grateful. A job of any kind was hard to come by now. And what would she do when the baby started showing? Perhaps they would let her stay on. But what about later—when the baby came?

Her thoughts always muddled there. She couldn't imagine actually having a baby—a child to care for, a real live day-to-day thing. She had written her parents and told them about the baby, about moving to a smaller apartment, too. But she made it sound cozy and convenient. She didn't complain. Even of how wretchedly she missed Alex. She wouldn't give her mother the satisfaction of one "I told you so." She smiled. She was acting a little like Adam Hutton. Proud and bullheaded. Well, she needed her pride. She had very little else to sustain her now.

Alex's check for November hadn't arrived yet. It worried her a little that it was late. It came direct from the government offices, she knew. Anything could go wrong where the government was concerned. It was less than two weeks till Christmas, and her small hoard of money was her only security against the winter. She didn't dare dip into it.

Oh, well. What did she need for Christmas, anyway? It was silly, but she'd wanted to buy some small thing for the baby and to send off a box to Alex and one to her folks. The money would come, but it was so hard to be patient.

Over three months now, and she still was feeling sick. She just had too much time to notice it, that was all. She'd have to keep busier. Buy some yarn and start on a blanket for the baby. That would be fun. Though it's easy to knit and think at the same time.

Someone opened the drugstore door, and a cold draft shook her. *I wonder what Alex is doing right now?* she thought. It's hot where he is and humid, not cold and blowy. It was so hard to imagine what it was like thousands of miles away on some tropical island. She knew from Alex's letters that the islands were teeming with men and activity, that building projects were going up everywhere, that the land was green, the climate mild and lovely, the Quonset hut a decent place to live. She knew that eight of the ten men in Alex's hut were married, and that very few Japs were left on the islands now, that there were movie theatres and ball diamonds for the men—all kinds of relaxation activities.

She also knew that Alex had already been on missions, flying with ten other men out over the ocean, all the way to the mainland of Japan. Six or seven hours to their target, an hour at most over land, then six hours home, or more if the Jap fighters followed them too closely, or if the plane got too shot up and just staggered along. She also knew that they flew home from the missions at night, alone in the darkness, above the darker water, praying that nothing went wrong, that they had enough fuel. Julia couldn't let herself think about it too long.

Alex claimed he loved it and minimized the dangers, explaining the "buddy system" and safeguards like that. To Julia it was an ominous, unknown nightmare, dark and evil and out of her control.

So she lived from day to day, sometimes hour to hour, and prayed a lot; somehow the days went by. And every day, safely lived and folded behind them, was, in itself, a kind of victory.

*   *   *   *   *   *

Ten days until Christmas. Activity was minimal. Maybe the change would be good for him after all. He didn't mind flying back to Honolulu, spending time with the general, having good food to eat. There was just one uncertainty hovering over him: What about Lillie, what did she have in mind?

One way or the other, he had no choice in the matter. The general gave the orders, and he obeyed. As long as he was going back to Hawaii he'd buy a gift or two and send them to Julia. They wouldn't make it for Christmas, but that was all right. A surprise just out of the blue would do her good. It comforted him to think about pleasing Julia; thoughts of her usually brought him so much pain.

There was too much blasted dead time on this island, hours and hours with nothing at all to do. Men would lie on their bunks for days and not lift a finger. It gave him the willies. When the holidays were through, he planned to volunteer for every mission they'd give him. That was far healthier than dying of jungle rot on his bunk. Maybe some men could turn off their minds; he couldn't. Action was his only hope for survival here.

*   *   *   *   *   *

The snow was lovely, soft, and sighing and sweeping. It covered the dirty streets and the yellowed yards, the unpainted fences, the heaps of uncleared rubbish; mercifully it covered every scar with a blanket of beauty, sparkling and white.

Julia sat on the couch, huddled beneath a blanket, and watched the snow till her eyes began to burn. She had a cold, and her head felt light and dizzy. She had no appetite, but her stomach hurt, and she knew she'd be in trouble if she left it empty.

It was two days until Christmas. Just two more days. A package had come from her mother. She looked at the presents, so prettily wrapped, set out beneath her tree. It was a little tree and scantily decorated. She almost didn't get it but then decided that she couldn't live through Christmas without a tree. That was the end of the road—the very bottom—where orphans and street urchins and old and dying widows lived storybook lives that made little children cry and rush from their bedrooms to gaze at their own bright trees and the piles of pretty presents stacked beneath. She hadn't sunk down to the storybook ending yet.

She shuddered. She could feel the fresh cold come in through the window glass. She wrapped the blanket more tightly but didn't move. Alex's service check had never come. She didn't know why. And what could she do about it? Two days before Christmas, and she was sick and alone, terribly homesick, and terribly afraid.

She didn't hear the door until the polite knocking became a pounding that broke her reverie. Quickly she slipped from the couch, feeling slightly dizzy, wishing she had time to run a comb through her hair. No one ever came to see her. To begin with, she didn't know very many people. And she was hesitant to talk about where she lived. Vera and Celia didn't even have her address yet.

When she opened the door, her very first impression was of a bulky black bear shaking snow on her newly-swept rug. A bear that growled and rumbled beneath his breath. She moved back a step or two, and then she saw him. She saw the face and realized who it was.

By this time he was inside, and she couldn't stop him. She closed the door against the icy air and met the cold, hard eyes without flinching. At last he had to speak, since she refused to.

"You're a difficult girl to find." He lifted an eyebrow. "If that's any satisfaction."

He took a chair, easing himself into the comfort, untying his scarf, unbuttoning the furry, bulky coat. Julia stood by the door and watched him.

"Well, Julia, I've gone to a lot of trouble to find you. I hope that it's worth it, for both our sakes."

She turned a little white, and her eyes blazed at him.

"All right, all right." He waved a tired hand. "I know how you feel. But I'm here. So don't act like a child, dear. Make the most of the situation."

She cut back every biting remark that came to her lips, all the angry, hurting things she wanted to say. She stood glaring at him, hating him in her heart.

"What do you want? You have five minutes," she said.

"Five minutes." Adam laughed far back in his throat. "Adversity hasn't softened you, my girl."

He paused, regarded her sharply, then shook his head.

"Listen, Julia, let's look at the facts together. You married my only son against my will. You forced my hand. You know what measures I've taken."

Julia started trembling inside. She moved and sat down, hating the show of weakness but knowing at the same time that she had no choice. He waited until she was settled and then continued.

"You have no husband, you have no money, you have no future. Tomorrow will not improve, I can promise you that."

He fumbled in his pocket and drew out a wallet, a long, leather, expensive-looking piece. Julia watched in horrible fascination as he drew out bill after bill, crisp and green and set them in a pile on the table beside him.

"Here's money to take you home, to your father and mother."

The bills kept coming, one by one, as he talked.

"Money for a ticket home and more—much more."

He paused and folded the wallet, but his eyes didn't seek hers.

"It's Christmastime, Julia. You're lonely and young and alone. Go home, where you can be happy . . . where you belong."

"Get out of here."

She spoke the words very softly. But she moved and opened the door, and the cold swept in. Adam Hutton rose and walked calmly past her. He shut the door and stood with his back against it.

"Don't let your pride get in the way of your reason, Julia. This is the only reasonable thing to do."

He inclined his head; his eyes were cold and piercing.

"There's a great deal of money there," he said.

Julia stood facing him still, though she rested her hand on the sofa.

"Five minutes, Julia. Will you take the money, my dear?"

She was feeling sick; she swallowed back the sickness.

"Come, Julia. Do I need to remind you again? You have no—"

"That's enough." Her voice was shaking. But Julia was past caring now. "You are wrong, pathetically wrong. It is you, Adam Hutton, who has allowed your passion to blind your reason. I have no money, that much is true."

He was watching her like a hawk, like a huge black vulture.

"But I have a husband, in spite of all you can do. And I have something more, Mr. Hutton. I have his child."

She paused; he didn't reply but stood staring at her.

"So that much was real. I thought perhaps Alex invented it just to get Lewis to grant him a leave."

His words were low; they weren't addressed to Julia. He shook his great dark head, and his eyes grew reflective.

"So you carry his child. No wonder you wax so brave."

He turned and crossed to the table and scooped up the money. He held it toward her as he walked back.

"All the more reason to take this," he stated bluntly. "You can't afford false pride any longer now. You have someone else to think of besides yourself."

"You act as though I have choices, and you have none. You *choose* to punish Alex, to punish me—even to punish yourself. You do it *on purpose!* Don't try to deceive yourself; that's a coward's way."

He seemed to cringe at her words or at least to grow scowly. But Julia swept on, determined to finish now.

"If you choose to punish Alex's son, that's your own matter. We'll get by; I'll care for this child somehow."

She drew herself up and swallowed and took a deep breath now.

"I choose to be here when Alex returns, Mr. Hutton. I'm his wife, and I love him. I will not run away."

Her voice was beginning to quiver. She strove to control it.

"I just pray that you, in your cold, blind anger, haven't snatched him away from both of us for good!"

The thought was spoken; the unadmittable horror. She saw the fear leap into his angry eyes. He turned and opened the door and left her. She stumbled onto the couch and lay there crying, calling out to Alex in the cold and empty room.

*   *   *   *   *   *

How did I let this happen? Alex wondered. *She's too quick for me,* he thought unhappily. An innocent Christmas Eve party at General Gordon's and now, suddenly, he was here in Lillie's car, with three other couples and Lillie pressed close against him, headed for the swankiest night spot in Honolulu. Trickery and fast thinking. But that didn't matter. He had no business being here at all.

The long car pulled up to the curb with a lurch and a screech of tires. Jack was already three sheets to the wind; he had no business driving. What a mess the rest of the evening promised to be.

The enlisted men lounging beneath the bright lights of the *Blue Heron* watched the fancy car with hungry interest. The prettiest girls on the island were officers' girls. The honey blonde who slid out from the back of the Chevy convertible was one of the very prettiest of them all.

"That's General Gordon's car, and that's his daughter." The man next to Marc smelled of cheap beer, and his voice was garbled.

"Who's the lucky sucker that's with her? I'd like to have her cling that way to me."

The soldier laughed and poked his friend with his elbow.

"Not sure. A flier. Name of Hutton, I think."

"He's a handsome devil, ain't he? A first lieutenant."

The first man rubbed his chin and swore with color.

"He's one of the general's little favorites. He'll be a captain within a month or two is my bet."

"Well, he's got the general's daughter, so it don't make much difference."

170

They laughed. Marc watched the couple the two were discussing. He didn't go in much for blondes, himself. But she was awfully pretty and terribly sexy. They walked very close to where Marc was standing. The young officer steered the girl expertly past and nodded and smiled at Marc in a friendly manner. He liked the officer's looks, but the general's daughter, close up, looked like she could be quite the little witch. Marc wouldn't want any part of her, anyway.

"Hutton." The drunk man spat, still watching the couple. "I hate these rich kids whose old men buy 'em into the army.

Officers, hell! They're no better'n you and me."

The glittering doors of the *Blue Heron* swung shut; the soldiers shrugged now and turned to look for other sights.

These miseries are more than may be borne!..
It is war's prize to take all vantages:
Look down and see what death is doing...
SHAKESPEARE

13

January 1945. One more year of war closed and ended. Surely this year ought to bring the peace. In November Roosevelt had been returned to the White House for an unprecedented fourth term. Three weeks after his inauguration he attended an important conference at Yalta where a series of agreements were made for the management of postwar Europe and Asia, agreements which were to have long-reaching and far-reaching results. So some people were beginning to hope and to tell themselves that a new year could bring anything—even, perhaps, the miracle of peace.

For Julia, January was long and dreary. Short days and long cold nights. Money running low, and no one to talk to. She could feel the baby moving within her now. It seemed more real, more part of her, more alive. But there was no one to come home to, no one to greet her. More battles, more awful numbers of wounded and dead. Handsome young faces staring out of the newsprint, cold and frozen forever, statistics now. She shuddered; she could not stand to look at the faces.

For Oscar Clayton, going over the last year's records, January posed a threat of more of the same ahead. Too bad Adam Hutton lacked the wisdom his young son had; too bad he had sent such a poor man to replace that son. Oscar had done his best to support Clarence Johnson, but the man was proving worse with time.

He wondered how Alex was faring, anyway, and how that pretty young wife of his was doing. He ought to get in touch with her now and then, just to make sure she was all right. But then, he supposed, Alex had taken good care of that.

Well, he'd do his best to iron out some of the problems at the plant and hope '45 would be better than '44. It was always better to have a positive attitude, though, he had to admit, he surely missed the boy.

January posed no promise for Adam Hutton. He missed his son much more than he'd thought he would. There seemed little purpose now to his profit-making, to his wheeling and dealing, to his brilliant business moves. Alex appreciated that sort of thing and was as apt a pupil as Adam had ever seen. But Alex wasn't here. And that reality pressed down on Adam more and more each day.

He wished he'd hear from the boy, just a note now and then. But he knew how stubborn he was. And one thing he'd say for Alex. He wasn't any sort of a hypocrite. He wouldn't write nice things just to placate his father. No, he wouldn't say something soft and nice unless he meant it. And he wasn't the sort to write bitter, vindictive letters. So, maybe there wasn't much he could do after all.

Things were getting pretty hot in the Pacific. Adam followed the papers with extreme and meticulous care. Alex was clever. He'd always been able to take care of himself. That's what Adam told himself, over and over, and most of the time it worked. Most of the time. The rest of the time was hell.

When the knock came at the door, Julia felt herself shudder. Ever since that snowy December evening when she had opened the door to find Adam Hutton there she had been a little wary when anyone knocked.

This time the shock was as great, perhaps even greater than it had been two days before Christmas. But this time she smiled and took the extended hand and hugged the haggard frame for a moment or two, very aware of her own changed and bulkier proportions.

"Marc! However in the world did you find me?"

He grinned, but it was a slow grin and rather sad.

"When I learned I'd be coming home via California, I wrote your folks to get your right address, then made arrangements to stop in Salt Lake City. Simple, really."

"Yes, yes, I guess so."

Julia pushed back some wisps of hair with nervous fingers. Marc was watching her, a little too closely she felt.

"I see you're . . . well . . ."

"Yes, I'm going to have a baby. End of May. In springtime."

"That will be nice. Have you been all right, Julia?"

"Yes, yes, I've been fine, Marc."

He didn't think she looked like she'd been fine. She had lost weight, in spite of the child that was coming. Her face looked gaunt, and her eyes looked very tired. It was strange. For in spite of all that, she looked lovelier than before.

"You look beautiful, Julia," he told her honestly. "Even more than I'd remembered in all this time."

"You look well yourself. In spite of . . . in spite of the war."

She thought his eyes looked haunted, very dark, almost

dull compared to the lights she'd remembered in them.

"I'm all right. You get used to a lot of things over there."

Julia nodded. "You were hurt?"

"Yeah, I took my number and lost. But I was luckier than most. I'll drag a bum leg around for the rest of my life and a pin in my shoulder. But I can live with that."

Julia nodded again. They gazed at one another. Just looking. Because so much of what they thought was too hard to say.

"I'm glad, Marc, you're home now and safe and . . . and that's behind you."

He nodded again, thinking, *Sure, but what's ahead? What's waiting for me with you in Utah, sitting here alone, waiting for some other man.*

"This guy you married, Julia? What's he like? I mean, well . . . I know it's none of my business . . ."

"It's all right, Marc. I know what you're trying to ask me. I guess you've a right to know if I'm really happy."

She told him about Alex, and her eyes began to sparkle, and the terms she used were more glowing than she knew. He watched her, something inside him growing angry. He hadn't thought it would be this hard.

"Alex is in the Pacific," she said at last, "though I suppose you would never have known one another. He flies B-29's out of Saipan." She rose. "Here's his picture. You may have seen him. Somewhere, sometime . . ."

She held out the ornate frame. The man that smiled from the photo was very handsome. His eyes were warm. His face looked intelligent, kind. He didn't wear a uniform. But the eyes, and the name, and the smile . . . suddenly everything came together.

Not sure. A flier. Name of Hutton, I think . . . Honey-blonde hair, eyes like a witch's eyes, the kindly young lieutenant who said hello . . . *Well, he's got the general's daughter, so it don't make much difference . . .* Hutton! Alex Hutton. *Marc, you're a fool! Why didn't you put the two together before?*

"Marc, what's the matter? Stop looking that way. What's the matter?"

He stared up at her, trying instantly to decide, wondering what to do, torn by emotions.

"You've seen him, haven't you? Tell me, what's wrong with Alex?"

Her hand was on his arm, clenching hard and tight. The fear in her eyes was terrible to see.

"Julia, I don't know Alex. I've hardly seen him. And as far as I know, I swear the guy's all right. He's safe. I swear it."

"Then what's the matter?"

"What in the heck do you mean?" He set down the picture. "I told you, Julia, I never knew the guy."

"But you looked at him as though you were seeing a ghost. Why, Marc?"

"Julia, drop it, all right, just drop it."

Marc could feel a line of sweat break out on his forehead. He felt small inside and trapped and scared. Part of him wanted desperately to tell her, some mean little urge to hurt her, some voice that said, *The rich guy's not taking good care of your little Julia. Who's to say you can't win her back again?*

She was pressing him now. If only she wouldn't press him. Give him time to push back the voices in his head.

"Where did you see him, Marc? Tell me!"

One of the voices broke and started to babble.

"At the swankiest officers' nightclub in Honolulu on the arm of a luscious blonde. And the little blonde beauty was acting chummy, very chummy indeed."

Her face went a little white, but she didn't answer. She sat

176

down on a chair, very carefully. She sat silent, her hands in her lap, and didn't move.

"Come on, Julia. It isn't the end of the world."

She didn't look up; she didn't move.

"Heck, it probably didn't mean a thing."

She shook her head. The white lips moved. Marc leaned a little closer.

"Perhaps with Alex it was innocent—I know it was. But it wasn't with her, and it wasn't with her father. Or with Alex's father, either, for that matter."

She looked up at last, great tear drops in her eyes.

"I didn't think he'd go that far. I should have known better. I should have known he wouldn't stop at anything."

Marc was frightened now. He eased himself out of the chair, then bent his one good leg and knelt beside her.

"Julia, honey, what are you talking about?"

She had only told him of Alex, not of Adam. She told him now, and he listened incredulously.

"You've got yourself mixed up in quite a mess here, Julia."

She smiled through her tears. "I've a knack for that it seems."

"I thought you were crazy over that blond guy, Nolan—the salesman."

"I tried to tell you it wasn't Nolan, Marc. It was the gospel, it was—"

"Yeah. Well, it doesn't matter, does it? Not now. Not ever again."

He eased back up, the joints in his bad leg aching, and sat beside her on the couch. He put his arm around her shoulders. He could feel her trembling, like a small, hurt bird. He pulled her gently close.

"This Hutton guy? Is he really that vicious, Julia?"

She nodded, relaxing against him, the trembling stilled. *What in the world has she gone through?* Marc wondered. He felt a pain, a burning deep inside.

"Marc, you're a man." She looked up, eyes wide and trusting. "You've seen Lillie Gordon. You know what war is like. Do you think, well . . . if it were you . . . do you think that Alex . . ."

She felt too ashamed of herself to continue. Marc tilted her head and looked into her tear-stained eyes.

"I think if I were Alex Hutton and you belonged to me, no girl alive could ever make me forget it. I mean that, Julia."

The tears spilled out of her eyes again.

"Besides, I've seen him, remember? Looked into his face. I think you can trust Alex, Julia. I think it's all right."

She hid her face against his shoulder until the tears would go away. When she looked up again, her eyes were no longer tortured, but the concern he read there made an aching feeling start far back in his throat. He pulled back his arm and drew away a little.

"Well, I guess we've settled just about everything. I guess I'd better—"

"Oh, no, you don't, Marc Sullivan. You're not going to help me like that and then run away. Both you and I need to laugh a little."

She reached down beside the couch and searched through her purse.

"Here, these are the keys to Alex's car. There's a grocery store at the corner, not very far. I'll tell you what I need."

She was up and moving, eyes warm and happy. Marc rose, too. Slowly, feeling the pain in his leg.

"I'm fixing spaghetti, Marc, and Italian bread, and a fresh green salad, and your favorite dessert."

There was happiness in her voice. He stood and watched

178

her, savoring the sight, as he knew he must, knowing she no longer belonged to him. She belonged to Alex Hutton, and Alex would keep her, no matter what his father tried to do—no matter what heaven or hell combined to throw against her.

*　　*　　*　　*　　*　　*

It was better now. Alex was flying one of the highest quotas of missions, and as junior officer in a "lead crew," he was going to school from morning till night on his off-flight days. He wasn't interested in the two hundred movie theatres or the boxing matches held every week. He'd play volleyball and swim with the guys some but mainly as a way to keep in shape. He had seen too many guys go "pineapple crazy"; he wanted no part in that kind of thing. It had taken him awhile, but he had a routine now that kept him busy and thinking every day, and he stuck to it rigorously. Only at night when he read the scriptures or wrote to Julia would the reality sometimes sweep over him like a wave, leaving him limp and drained and shaken. But usually, through rigid discipline, he was okay.

It had been tough for awhile when he first came back to the islands. Even though he had been firm with Lillie at Christmas, he hadn't seemed to get the message through. She and the general together had their caps set for him, and he began to find it hard to be polite, to find ways to refuse their offers without offending.

Sometimes Lillie preyed on his mind, and he couldn't forget her; she was part of the singsong, sweet island lethargy, the sensuous, sun-drained lack of reality there. On Christmas day she had caught him alone for a moment and kissed him in the old way, hungry, soft, and demanding. It had shaken him to feel the response she could still engender, to see longing mingled with triumph in her eyes.

He thought of it now as he sat along the runway, watching the planes that were leaving on missions take off. It was crazy how the men gathered and sat on mounds, on bulldozers parked along the runway, even on buildings, to wave and encourage, to watch their comrades leave. Even after so many times, Alex felt himself being caught up in the scene before him.

As the big machines taxied along, the spacing between them was perfect; there was seldom a blank spot, seldom a delay. As one rose into the air, a few feet above them, another would be in line to take its place. After seconds a plane taking off was out over the water, the pilot nosing low to gain more speed, too low for sight beneath the jutting cliffs. Then soon the planes would edge up into sight again.

He watched, wondering what would become of today's short flying—how many planes would return, how many go down, how many just disappear, heaven knows where. In fifteen hours or less it would all be over, and they'd be back—the ones who were coming back, that is.

He remembered the mission he'd flown three weeks ago—an "abort" they called it. He'd blown a cylinder head within half an hour of Tokyo. He turned around and limped back, in the air for fourteen hours, without even getting credit for a mission. That was the way of it. An abort was better than ditching any day. Most aborts made it safely back to base. Only one-fifth of the crews that ditched were ever rescued.

He shaded his eyes and watched the sleek silver missiles shrink and turn into specks in the distance, then merge and disappear until there was nothing but sea and sky, an endless expanse of blue.

* * * * * *

On a day in late March Julia sold the cream and brown Packard. As Adam had promised, no money ever came. She had to have some way to pay for the baby, some way to get by in the days when she couldn't work. She had put it off, postponed it as long as she dared. Finally she advertised it, and the ad ran for weeks with very few lookers. A car that expensive had a limited market, she knew. She had no phone, so she'd had to list the address of the apartment. That frightened her, but she knew no other way.

Her apartment was actually one side of a duplex. A middle-aged couple, the Roberts, lived in the other half. Frank Roberts was a taciturn man but tolerably friendly, except for the times he got drunk and beat up on his wife. Leah Roberts, though outside-tough, had a heart that was tender and did little neighborly things to watch out for Julia. These last few weeks, when Julia had felt uncertain, Leah had come out with her to question prospective buyers.

This particular morning Julia didn't bother to stop by for Leah. The gentleman who came to the door wore a short tweed coat, leather driving gloves, and a natty hat cocked on his head. He had a trim moustache and a cultured accent. He was fifty, perhaps fifty-five. Julia threw on a coat and took him outside to the Packard, feeling perfectly safe with the man.

He examined the car very thoroughly, every inch of it, running a hand appreciatively here and there, making pleasant murmurs beneath his breath. Yes, Julia assured him, the mileage reading was accurate. One owner, not driven much during the past six months. She brought out Alex's service and upkeep records; the man nodded and hummed approvingly.

"She's a honey, all right, and well worth what you're

asking."

He drew out his wallet and started to count out cash. Julia tried to keep the surprise she felt from showing. When he had reached the required sum, he kept on counting until two extra crisp fifty dollar bills lay in Julia's hand. She offered them back to the man, beginning to protest. But he took her small hand in his two gloved hands with a fatherly pat.

"No, my dear, you keep it. That's still a fair price."

He smiled; there were dozens of smile lines around his eyes.

"Buy something for yourself and for the new baby."

She watched him climb into the car and start the engine. It purred beneath his hand. He rolled down the window and stuck out his head.

"Needless to say, I'll take good care of her for you. Don't worry about the car a bit."

He backed down the long narrow drive and into the street. Julia watched until the car was out of sight. She was glad, after all, that she hadn't stopped by for Leah. The tears were running shamelessly down her cheeks, and she wouldn't have wanted Leah see her cry.

*   *   *   *   *   *

Spring chose to come early and warm that year, scattering scents of earth and green and growing—tantalizing, promising, wonderful smells! Julia felt the lift in the air and responded to it. She felt part of the birth, the renewal, the newness around her. She carried her own inner promise, her own new spring, her own guarantee of continuance into tomorrow.

Since she'd sold the Packard, she'd done a lot more walking, so she was grateful for the mild days, the gentle air. She was feeling a little milder herself, more at peace now. She had spent the past Sunday with Vera and Celia; those two could always warm her and lift her spirits. Surely spring and birth would defeat death and dying. Her parents had hinted that they might make a trip out to see the baby. The war in Europe was drawing to a close. There were promises made now in every paper, in every announcement, in every speech. Surely, now the promises would come true!

She thumbed through the paper still dreamy, still hardly thinking. When she came to the pages of casualties, her heart gave its usual leap. But she never looked through those pages. She started to skip them, then gasped and rose and threw the paper from her, as though it had been some serpent coiled on her lap and had risen cruelly, suddenly to strike. She stood there, trembling all over, then stomped on the paper.

"No!" she cried out, "No! No!"

After long minutes, she dropped to her knees and drew up the pages. Her fingers were shaking. She smoothed out the crumpled sheets. *Please,* she prayed, *let me be wrong. Please don't let it be there.*

There were dozens of handsome faces set out on the pages—some smiling, some solemn, looking young, so very young. She closed her eyes, unable to scan the faces, unable to confront what would happen if she saw—

As soon as she opened her eyes the picture was before her. How could she have missed it? It leaped out from all the others. The face was one of the handsomest faces there. And the eyes. Even in black and white newsprint the eyes held a sparkle.

She shook the face, but the beautiful eyes kept smiling. Frozen in black and white, never blue again. Never moving over her face, never laughing at her. The blue eyes, the blond hair, the musical voice. *I'll be all right. I lead a charmed life, remember? Remember . . . remember . . .* She screamed at the picture.

"Nolan, please don't die! Please, you promised! Nolan . . . please, Nolan . . ."

She couldn't see the picture; it was blurred, it was lost, the tears were choking her throat. She lay on the floor and wept beside the picture, and there was no promise singing inside her now. Just a terrible bitterness and pain past bearing, a pain that all her tears wouldn't wash away.

He is mine only son, and heir to the lands of me,
O my son, my son! Tell me—where is my son?
SHAKESPEARE

—————————————————————————————14

The miracle came. May 7. The radios blared it, each town had banners, fireworks, and parades. The papers plastered headlines and smiling faces. Victory in Europe! V-E Day!

Julia watched strangers cry in the streets and embrace each other and laugh and shout with a wild relief and joy. She stood at her window and watched, but she felt no gladness. Only a numbed wonder, a deep and quiet awareness that in countries and cities whose names she couldn't pronounce the dying would stop now, the young, handsome faces come home; the statistics would dwindle and people start living again.

It was good. But all she could think of was Nolan's picture, of the wives and mothers whose brave men would not return, of the oceans of tears that would not give them a tomorrow, of the thousands for whom the victory came too late. It was stupid, destructive to think about it that way, in terms of individual human suffering. But she couldn't help it. Besides, in the Pacific there was no victory yet. The dying went on. The wounded and killed, the faces, the statistics. So for Julia the nightmare went on still, it had not ended. Except that hope, cruel hope, had laid its hand on her heart.

The doctor had been saying "any day" for two weeks now. Julia had thought of calling Vera, but what would she say? There was really nothing to do till the baby started coming. She just hoped she would know when that was! Older women all smiled and said, "Oh, you'll know, dear. Don't fret about that." Leah had offered her help and the use of her telephone—anytime, whatever the hour. There was nothing really to do but wait.

On May 18 Leah's mother called her. Her father had slipped from a ladder while painting the house. They thought he had broken his back. Could she come right away? Leah was ready within the hour. She brought Julia a key.

"My folks just live in Ogden. I won't be gone long, dear. I daren't be. I can't trust Frank by himself."

She kissed her and gave her a squeeze. "Now, honey, don't have this baby till I get back."

Julia smiled and watched her go. *As far as I'm concerned,* she thought to herself, *the sooner this baby comes, the better.*

But she didn't feel so certain later that evening when her labor pains began to come. At first she wasn't certain that this was the thing. She waited, but by the hour the contractions grew stronger, more regular, more evenly spaced. It was now past midnight. She thought of Leah's apartment. But Frank would be there, and Frank had been drinking, she knew. If she awoke him in the night, in the muddled darkness, he might take her for Leah. She shuddered at the thought. She knew how Frank could be when he was drunk. She had heard through the walls; she had talked in the mornings to Leah.

So she bathed and washed her hair and checked the few things she had packed for the hospital stay, then sat by a dim light and waited out the hours. She felt a sad little longing to phone her mother. If only her mother could come right away, appear by her side, hold her hand, and soothe her fears. But a telephone call would end in dull silence again, reminding her just how far away she was.

She thought of Alex, but that kind of thinking was painful. What would tonight be like if Alex were here? Would he be calm or would he panic and fuss around her, trying to hide his own alarm? She didn't know. She had no way of knowing. They hadn't experienced much together. There hadn't been time. *Would there ever be time again?* The question popped into her head; she chased it back into the shadows. Surely a girl shouldn't have her first baby alone!

The pains were coming hard, very hard now. She checked the clock. It ought to be light in an hour. When the light came, she would chance it and go call Vera. If Frank woke up, at least he would see that she wasn't Leah . . .

It was light. There were no more shadows in the corners. She turned the key, and the door opened with a creak. She heard Frank mumble and turn. She froze a moment. Then his snores began again. She crept into the quiet kitchen and dialed Vera's number. She almost wept when she heard the sane, normal voice.

"How long? I will not wait until after breakfast! You collect your things, Julia, and wait for me on the porch. I'll be there in a shake."

Julia sighed with relief, crept back out, and locked the door behind her, hearing the faint, irregular snoring still. It was chilly, but the day was dawning fresh and lovely. She winced and tried to walk upright in spite of the pains. She was sitting on the porch, a small huddled figure, when Vera pulled up a few minutes later.

In Julia's mind the details would always be fuzzy. The trip with Vera, the doctors, the labor room. All she could think of was being brave and not screaming. Vera kept saying, "Be patient, dear, it won't be much longer." Dr. Stevens would pat her arm with a gentle hand.

There were times she wanted to scream at the kindly faces; there were times all she wanted was to be left alone. She could read pity in their eyes, and she hated pity. She closed her own eyes and pictured Alex's face. But the face was much too dim, the face would leave her, melt away and disappear and leave her alone. And when she opened her eyes again, there was no Alex.

She was dimly aware when they wheeled her into the delivery room. And after that it was really no time at all till she heard the doctor laugh and a faint cry answer—a long, high sound that ended with a shudder. She opened her eyes.

"You have a son, dear. A beautiful, healthy baby boy."

She opened her arms. Dr. Stevens nodded to the nurse beside her, and a small, warm bundle was placed against her side. She touched his cheek. The innocent eyes gazed at her. He moved his mouth as though he wanted to speak. How soft, how incredibly soft his skin was! He had a shock of dark, straight hair. He was beautiful!

She heard a sound and realized she was crying. Somebody took the baby. And now the tears, held back for days, for weeks, for months now, at last the cleansing tears began to come.

* * * * * *

It was Monday, and the mail planes would be coming. But Alex wouldn't be back until Monday night. He was flying out on a mission early that morning. He hoped some word would come about the baby. Surely by now . . . Well, perhaps when he got back, something would be waiting for him.

Eleven men in a B-29; the space was crowded, especially

since so much of the inside was taken up with gas tanks and bomb racks. Some men would catch a few hours of sleep in the tunnel, thirty feet long, just big enough to crawl through. Alex couldn't stand the cramped, airless space. He'd take a nap in his seat if he had to.

The men had eaten all the fried eggs they wanted for breakfast—special mission-day rations. The lunches were packed: sandwiches, oranges, and cookies to eat on the way. The planes were checked and fueled and loaded. Everything was green light, ready to go.

In minutes they were out and over the water. It would be hours now before they sighted land, before the few tense moments of action, to justify their being here at all. The men laughed and talked and told friendly jokes; the hours began slowly to pass.

Julia had sent off a little picture of the baby, with all his statistics, with all the facts of his birth, packed in with the longest letter she'd ever yet written! How she wished she could see Alex's face.

It was incredible how well she was feeling, how much her old self. And little Alexander was such a good baby, so easy for her to take care of. In fact, she couldn't get enough of him yet. Even when he slept, she would stand and watch him, note the features that were Alex, the ones that were her. Marvel at how complete and perfect he was.

She had debated what to do about Adam. Should she send an announcement, just to let him know? What emotions would he feel when he discovered he had a grandson? Pride struggled with disdain, and she hesitated. So now, two weeks later, Adam still didn't know of the baby.

She picked up the little bundle and held him close. He

closed his tiny hand around one of her fingers. She buried her face against his fragrant skin, marveling at the joy he made her feel.

They were in trouble. Alex knew it and tried not to panic, tried to think straight. It had all seemed to happen so quickly. They had hit the target, but then they had been hit. He had felt the impact and heard the muffled explosion. They dropped down and turned around to start back alone. But the Jap fighters spotted a cripple and started coming. Three Alex counted . . . four . . . five. He heard the copilot swear beneath his breath. One engine was already out, and three crew members hurt badly, the bombardier with one leg blown clear away. Alex could feel something burning along his own leg, and his foot felt on fire, but he didn't have time to check.

The plane was riddled with holes, but he kept her flying. He radioed for help. They were down to two engines. The air was full of other calls of distress. He wondered if there was a plane close enough to help them.

There was a roaring sound far back in Alex's head. He shook it off and checked the instrument panel. *Easy going. Calm down,* he told himself. One minute at a time. The plane kept going. The horizontal stabilizers were gone. He could only keep control by using his motors. One more minute, ten minutes, half an hour.

Alex was aware of nothing except the plane, concentrating all his limited powers on one thing: Keep the plane upright and going on. The plane kept falling into a right spiral and, with a sickening sensation, he'd lose control. He would radio: "In right spiral and out of control now." But somehow he'd pull her out of it again.

For hours it seemed the pattern kept repeating. Each time

they spun into a spiral, they thought it would be their last. Alex could barely see now. His head was throbbing. His shoulders were aching, his arms, his whole left leg. *Easy does it, easy.*

Some men were singing. From somewhere off behind him the muffled sounds came. It was a Civil War song, muted and melancholy. He could catch a note or two, then the sound would fade.

"We're tenting tonight on the old campground, thinking of days gone by . . . loved ones at home . . . . gave us the hand . . . . tear . . . said good-bye . . ."

Alex heard the crack and felt the terrible wrenching. There wasn't time to radio this time. The plane was spiraling down, and he couldn't stop it. The last thing he remembered was seeing light—white and red and burning all around him. Then a growing darkness invaded the cockpit, a smothering darkness that pressed on his aching head.

It wasn't until late that night, back at base, that they took the tally—the final tally of the planes known lost and of the missing. The last bomber that was coming in had landed. The exciting stories were already being told. They had to talk, they had to tell the stories, before they could fall into a weary, oblivious sleep.

But one lone plane headed out into the darkness, moving steadily northward. He would be there. When dawn blew the night stars away and the sun was rising, he would be there—in the area where the ditchings had been reported. Two ditchings, two lost bombers, twenty-two men. He would be there, with morning, to look for his stranded friends.

One ditching in five recovered. The spotter pilot had searched the water against the blinding sun. He saw no bodies. He saw no wreckage. He circled the area once; he circled again. No sign of survivors.

Perhaps someone had misheard the readings. Mistakes were so easy over static air waves, in the middle of battle and fear. But if they weren't down below, it was any man's guess. *How did he get rid of this empty feeling inside his chest?*

He widened his circle, he stared till his eyes were burning. The spotters with him came forward. They shook their heads. One swore and spat. There was nothing they could do now. The pilot turned his plane and headed back.

The general got the news in a matter of hours. At first he refused to believe it. He checked the report, he verified it once, and then again. For a long time he sat in his office and stared at nothing. Then he picked up the phone and began to make the call he had never thought he would have to make.

Adam Hutton, in his office, put back the receiver. Lewis had been as gentle as he could. Managed the matter with just the right mixture of tenderness and tact. Too much emotion Adam could never have handled. Too much—my God, it can't be! Other men's sons but not his own—not Alex! Not that much promise shot down, destroyed by some slant-eyed Jap.

He slammed his fist down hard against the desk top, again and again. A phrase had jumped into his head. It was ringing there. The words were Alex's, so was the voice that spoke them. So real the boy could have been standing right there beside him.

Nor you, Father. It's out of your hands, too. I hope to heaven you don't live to regret it.

He slammed his fist again, but the voice kept humming. And this time the face with the voice was a little boy's face, fresh and alive with intelligence, arms extended, running to him, running across the sand . . .

I hope to heaven you don't live to regret it, regret it, regret it.

There was a searing pain down low in Adam's chest. He banged his fist again till it bruised his fingers. He felt clammy all over; he couldn't catch his breath. The pain had become like an elephant's weight upon him, strangling his breathing, crushing down on his chest. He gasped for breath, the hard fist convulsed and then crumpled, as the massive man in the chair crumpled and fell.

* * * * * *

The very next morning, in Utah, Clarence Johnson waited impatiently for the boss's call. For the past few months now Adam had called him weekly for a personal accounting, a weekly report. Clarence bitterly resented this action; the obvious motives behind it he knew too well. So he said what he needed to keep the old man happy. To the devil with the time when the truth at last came out. He'd face that day when he reached it. Till then he could play the game as well as the next guy.

This morning the call from California was late. It made him nervous. He took a drink while he waited. Just one. To bolster his spirits. Ten minutes . . . twenty. This wasn't like Adam Hutton. At last the ring. Clarence took a deep breath. He waited through one more ring. When he picked up the phone, a woman's voice responded.

"Hello, this is Adam Hutton's secretary. I'm terribly sorry for the delay. But Alex has been shot down somewhere over the Pacific . . . No, his body has not been recovered. . . I'm sorry to report that Adam suffered a heart attack yesterday. . . Yes, he is still in critical condition . . . That would be recommended . . . Yes, carry on for the interim. You'll receive further instructions from this office as soon as possible . . . Yes, it may be awhile . . . Yes, thank you . . . yes, good-bye.''

Clarence Johnson put down the phone with a little snicker. Heck of a situation, this. He called in Oscar Clayton, the Mormon foreman, and told him the new developments. After he left, Clarence grabbed his jacket and bottle, locked the office, and disappeared for the rest of the day.

By mid-morning of the next day Clarence Johnson had still not shown up at the plant. Oscar Clayton was already discovering that some of his very worst fears were justified. Besides, an alarming call had come in that morning. He had to make a decision and right now. He made some calls—it took a little doing to find her. Then he drove to the address where Julia Hutton lived.

He was a little surprised; he'd expected a grander setting. This apartment was about as humble as it could be. He double-checked the address he had written. And, hoping it was right, he went to the door.

Julia opened the door herself. She looked as pretty and sweet as he'd remembered. She recognized him at once and invited him in.

"How are things at the plant?"

She asked half a dozen questions, innocent, interested. Oscar took off his hat and twirled it unconsciously in his nervous fingers. This was going to be mighty hard.

"Well, Sister Hutton, that's the reason why I'm here. The plant, you know. Till your father-in-law's back in commission . . .''

He paused, interrupting himself.

"And we certainly hope that's soon. Is he doing better? Have you heard further news?"

The young lady's expression looked startled and confused.

"I don't understand," she said. "Has something happened to Adam?"

"The heart attack, ma'am."

"What heart attack? When? What happened?"

Julia watched the man's face. She didn't want to alarm him. He could have no idea of how their relationship stood.

"I don't know about the heart attack. Please, please tell me."

He thought it rather strange that she shouldn't know yet. He was getting a funny feeling about the whole thing.

"Please," she urged, leaning a little toward him.

"Day before yesterday, ma'am. When he heard about Alex. They say he just collapsed in his office. They've had the electrocardiogram on him ever since. We haven't heard—"

He stopped himself. *What was happening here?* Julia's face had turned as white as chalk. She was slumped in her chair. She was staring at him strangely.

"Alex! Alex! Please tell me, what happened to Alex?"

What awful predicament had he blundered into?

"There must be some mistake, my dear. We'd better—"

"Please! Please tell me about Alex. No one has!"

Oscar Clayton was more than perplexed, he was terrified now. But he could see how real the girl's own anguish was. He took her hand and told her very gently, as he would have told a daughter of his own.

"His plane went down somewhere in the Pacific. Monday night, after a mission, apparently. His commander called Mr. Hutton Tuesday morning. They sent out spotters, but . . . nothing was ever found."

Her fingers were locked like vises around his own. Her face looked ghostly strange, but there were no tears yet. She nodded, as though acknowledging all he said.

"And they think he's dead?" Her voice was calm and quiet.

"Well, my dear. . .well. . ." Oscar clumsily stroked her hand.

"He's not dead, Mr. Clayton. I know he isn't." Her voice sounded strangely natural, not dull, not obsessed.

"I'd know if Alex were dead. Somehow I'd know it."

Oscar Clayton's heart went out to her now. "The chances are so slight . . . the chances . . ."

"I don't care about the chances or the odds. I don't care what anyone says. I won't believe it. He isn't dead. I know he isn't dead."

She began to rise. He dropped the hand he was holding. She crossed to the window and stood there looking out. When she turned back, her face was still pale, her eyes still tearless. And she seemed to be in control of herself.

"I'm sorry about Adam," she said gently, almost to herself. "I hope he doesn't die. And I pray to God we won't have to wait much longer."

She clenched her hands together, then let them drop. Her eyes looked a little too bright, but she smiled at Oscar. A very little smile that wrenched his heart.

"You came here for something. What was it you needed?"

He almost recoiled; he drew back in discomfort now.

"Oh, no, ma'am. I wouldn't think to impose upon you. Not now—not—no, I'm sorry—" He edged away.

"Don't be silly. It was something very important. Or you never would have come."

She moved and held out her hand.

"You thought I already knew. That's the only difference. But I wouldn't have known about Alex for long. And you came, anyway. So I know it must be important."

He hesitated. She seemed so strong, so sure.

"Please, Mr. Clayton, please sit down and tell me."

He did as she asked. He was almost afraid to oppose her. Afraid opposition might crack her uncanny calm. He told her about Clarence Johnson, told her quite gently, but her quick mind got to the meat of the matter fast.

"Shame on Adam," she scolded. "That's so very like him. Cut off your arm, but cut his own throat as well."

She laughed a hard little laugh and bid him continue.

"So, anyway, since the news came he's not been around. I don't expect to see him much . . ."

"Well, that's not really bad news. Heaven knows you can run the place much better yourself."

Her eyes were warm and sympathetic. He shook his head.

"You don't quite understand. I've no authorization. My hands are tied, ma'am."

She scowled a little. "Yes, yes, I hadn't thought about that."

"And you see, this morning a call came into the office. We've a chance on a job that would pull us clean out of this slump. A bid on some government work—a real honey. I hate to see it slip through our hands."

"But you aren't authorized to bid and to make that decision?"

He nodded. He could see that her own mind was turning now.

"If you had the job, could you handle it, could you turn out the product?"

It was his turn to frown.

"I think so, but I'm not sure. We're a little understaffed now, and this is a big one. It would be nice to have some temporary help. On some of the simpler, assembly line procedures."

Julia sat thinking and shaking her pretty head.

"I've half a dozen ideas already," she told him. "A Hutton signature would get you what you want. Right?"

He nodded slowly.

"For as long as we would need. By the time things were straightened out and the old man was back on his feet, the job could be done—"

"And you'd have saved Adam's neck."

She pursed her lips. She looked at him very closely.

"I'm willing to make a run for it. Are you?"

He returned her look, excited by what he saw there.

"It's a greater risk for you," she said, "than for me."

"I know that," he said. "I knew that before I came here."

"Well, then, if you're game, Oscar Clayton, so am I. Tell me where you want me to start."

Later that afternoon a startled Vera was tending the little sleeping Alexander, with a promise to keep him for several more days if needed. She had also given Julia a list of all the women in the ward and stake Relief Society.

"Here are your extra workers," Julia told Oscar Clayton. "I'm sure we'll be able to get what we need from here."

At the plant Oscar led her to Alex's office, which had never been used by Clarence Johnson, he stressed. She smiled thinly and asked him to leave her alone for a moment. He didn't like the idea, but in the end he closed the door and left her to herself.

Julia touched the familiar things, the things that were Alex, things that brought back floods of memory. She sat at his desk. She could almost feel him beside her. It was close to eerie: There were sheets with his signature on them, the pens he had used, his little paperweight. Julia felt a lonely aching deep inside her but not a sense of fear or loss or pain.

Is this one of those feared and yet predicted reactions? Am I refusing to accept the fact that Alex is dead? Will something finally break and let me know it? Am I lying to myself?

Julia didn't think so. The feeling inside her was much too warm, too real to be a mere defense, a stunned reaction. She felt calm and assured in a way she could not explain.

She dropped to her knees by the desk and prayed there, knowing she couldn't go through the next days alone. The strength within her grew, the warm assurance. *Walk by faith.* She never had done it before. But now that was the only path she could see before her. She set her foot on the path without hesitation, without any fearing, without any looking back.

Enough! I am engaged; I will challenge him . . .
Face to face, and frowning brow to brow.
SHAKESPEARE

—————————————————————— **15**

A dam Hutton hovered. The doctors would rouse him, then he would sink and fail again. The fighter had retreated somewhere inside him. The huge bulk of a man lay mute and unresponding. Both the will and the mind refused to function. They fed him, watched him, monitored his progress. Tenaciously his body held on. Slowly he stabilized, his condition improved. Slowly the physical responded. But the man himself was still hiding somewhere inside.

Monday, mid-afternoon, Clarence Johnson awoke. He had slept off his stupor. He rubbed his unshaven chin. It was Wednesday morning when he had walked out of the office. He probably ought to go back, check things out a bit, see if there was word yet on the old man.

He wasn't too concerned about his reception. These Mormons weren't complainers; they wouldn't rat. Besides, who was there to complain to beside Adam Hutton? Till Adam was back in the picture, they all could relax. Which is just exactly what Clarence intended to do.

The girl at the front desk looked uncertain when he walked in. He growled something at her and headed for his office.

"Just a moment, uh, Mr. Johnson, could you wait just a

moment?"

"What do you mean 'just a moment'? What the hell's going on?"

She had pressed a button somewhere under her desk top. Oscar Clayton appeared. He stood very close to Clarence.

"Would you please come with me, sir? Mrs. Hutton would like to see you."

"Mrs. Hutton?"

Clarence spurted and sputtered a little, but he followed the man to the big, wood-paneled office. The one they had never allowed him to use. The one with the shiny gold plate that read *Alex Hutton.*

Oscar Clayton opened the door. They walked inside. Behind the great desk, working busily over some papers, sat as pretty a woman as Clarence had ever seen. Her head was bent, her hair falling over her shoulders. Soft brown hair with the colors of sunlight in it, a dozen colors like sunlight on dappled leaves. She raised her head; he was shocked at her youthful features. Delicate skin, a full sensuous mouth. Wide eyes, deep and brown, eyes you could swim in. The big brown eyes were gazing into his eyes, reading much too deep. Clarence dropped his own bloodshot gaze. He ran a finger beneath his sticky collar.

"Mr. Johnson." Julia smiled, but the smile was icy. Clarence coughed and shifted a little. The woman did not invite him to sit down.

"I've been going over the plant records, Mr. Johnson." She indicated a stack by her left hand. "The facts I find are appalling."

She lifted an eyebrow. Clarence did not meet her eyes.

"How many days have you worked this month, Mr. Johnson?"

The question caught him a little by surprise.

"Well, I . . . I've been here most of the time. I've had some problems."

"Yes, Mr. Johnson. I am also aware of those."

The way she said it made Clarence tremble a little. *How much did she really know?*

"In May you were absent six days out of twenty. During April five out of twenty-two. In March you missed nine of the twenty-three work days."

She paused a moment, ruffling a paper or two.

"I don't think I need to take you back any further. I think we've satisfactorily illustrated the point, don't you?"

He looked up then. The eyes were not cold, but the eyes meant business.

"To say the least, you have failed an important trust. You've made a mess out of a business that Alex left humming, with production records that no other company topped."

She took a deep breath and then continued curtly.

"That, Mr. Johnson, is inexcusable." She paused, tapped the desk with her pen, and then continued.

"Though the news may not please you, Mr. Johnson, Adam Hutton is recovering nicely now. Of course, he'll be out of commission for awhile yet. So it will be some time before these figures will reach him."

She paused and looked him over once again.

"The choices, the decisions, the directions you've been giving have been very unwise, Mr. Johnson, to say the least. And I'm sorry to see that they've also been somewhat illegal. Not to mention morality, loyalty, or any of that."

Clarence had never been through this kind of wringer. He was beginning to resent the lady very much. If he wasn't so afraid of what she could do to him!

"As soon as legalities can be arranged, you'll hear from our lawyers. Until then, Mr. Johnson, consider yourself dismissed.

Miss Clarke at the front office will give you your severance pay."

Clarence saw red now.

"Hold on! You got no damn right . . ."

"I have every right, Mr. Johnson, and you know it! Don't push me, Mr. Johnson, don't even try."

The tone of her voice stopped him cold. There was something about her. He pulled back; he wasn't about to tackle her now.

"The severance check, by the way—as you, yourself, are aware—is merely one last courtesy on our part. Remember that."

She inclined her pretty head slightly.

"Good day, Mr. Johnson. Oscar will see you out."

Oscar winked at Julia over his shoulder as he left her. The admiration in his eyes was plain to see. It filled Julia's head with a sense of exultation, though she felt weak and trembly inside now that it was over.

Yet she had never before felt so pleased with herself! Alex would be proud if he could see her. She turned back to her papers and thought, somewhat smugly, with a great sense of satisfaction: *Adam would be, too!*

* * * * * *

The spotter plane had reached the site of the ditching, the radioed site where the wreckage ought to be. The pilot dipped down low. Nothing. But suddenly one of the crewmen shouted.

"What's that, over there?"

He swore softly in amazement. One huge chunk of ragged fuselage bobbed up and down, and hanging along it were two men—three men—no! There were four guys alive in the water down there!

It wasn't long till the rescue was in action. The men, badly hurt, were hauled up with extra care.

"By damn, we found 'em this time!" The crew was delighted, proud of themselves. One of them rose from bending over a stretcher, stood upright, and slapped his leg.

"Well, I'll be!"

"What's the matter?" another one asked him.

"This guy says his name is Moore. Billy Moore."

"So?"

"So, Moore's part of the crew that ditched on Monday. Monday, do you hear? These guys have been out here lost for two whole days now. This isn't the crew that radioed at all!"

The listener scratched his head, then shook it in wonder.

"You mean to tell me these guys are out here alive, sloshin' around an' just waitin' for us since Monday? I don't believe it."

"Tell Moore here that. Go ahead, tell 'im, Freddie."

Alex couldn't remember the ditching, or the rescue, or the trip to Honolulu. They told him the details, but nothing seemed to stick. He really had no recollection of the mission, nothing recent had stayed in his memory. In the fevered tossing, in the times when he seemed most conscious, all he did was call out Julia's name or talk to her in urgent, garbled phrases.

The doctors patched him up, examined him, did some testings. There was a definite concussion with probable cerebral edema and a nasty laceration and ecchymosis along his head. When he was lucid, he complained of terrible headaches and fuzzy vision. The fracture could easily be the cause of both.

204

The boy had some nasty abrasions along his leg as well as multiple fragmented fractures of the ankle bones. The surgeon wanted to pin the fractured ankle, though the procedure he recommended was fairly new. They fussed for days about the young captain, until General Gordon appeared and settled it all.

He was furious that he hadn't been notified sooner. Several people tried patiently to explain: "It was an unexpected rescue, rather a surprise, sir." "No one knew that you should be notified." "Sorry, sir, we didn't have that information."

Lewis Gordon had received a telegram from California. He knew of Adam's condition. He moved so fast, cut so much red tape that he almost became a legend.

"This soldier is being transferred to California. Priority medical attention. Top of the line."

Alex never realized what was happening. He woke up once and didn't know where he was. The next time he opened his eyes the room seemed different. They assured him he was still in an army hospital, all right. No, this wasn't Honolulu. No, it wasn't the islands, God forbid. *This* was California, in the good old U.S. of A!

They told him his son was alive. His eyelids flickered. They called his housekeeper, Maria, into the room.

"It's true, Mr. Hutton, it's true. Alexander's alive!"

She patiently went over every detail. The eyes stayed open. She retold each detail again. The eyes began to show expression. The man had returned; the man was beginning to fight.

"I want the woman brought here at once," the doctor

repeated.

"But, Mr. Hutton would never allow it, sir. If he knew—"

"We do not need permission for this, Maria. It is a critical medical necessity. It is my judgment, as the boy's attending physician. And, of course, I accept full responsibility."

The woman looked miserable; the doctor felt sorry. He patted her arm reassuringly.

"And, Maria, it is also medically expedient that we do not inform Adam about this decision right now."

She nodded. "Yes, sir."

"Do you have the girl's address then?"

"I can get it, sir."

"Well, then, what are you waiting for? Come on, woman, I haven't got time to wait here. I need that address, and I need it right now!"

It was a nuisance. Alex's wife had no telephone listing, only an apartment address. After a few ineffectual curses that didn't help much, Dr. Russell sent a personal telegram. What the heck, Adam Hutton had the money. He shouldn't concern himself about that.

Julia came back to the apartment late that evening. She had stayed to visit with Vera for awhile. The work at the plant was exciting, exhilarating. But she could feel the pressure of the demands, and she came home worn and exhausted every night.

She fed Alexander and tucked him into his covers, kissing his soft cheek, kssing his silken hair. She was just beginning to think about a shower when the doorbell rang. It startled her. Eight o'clock. Had she forgotten something? Had Oscar run into some trouble? She hurried to the door.

The uniformed boy held out the yellow envelope.

"Mrs. Hutton?"

Western Union, the sign on his uniform read. Julia felt a chill run along her backbone. She signed her name and thanked the boy and reluctantly took the message he still held. She closed the door. Her hands were shaking. *California* the return address read. Then it wasn't Alex! She didn't know whether to feel relief or disappointment. She tore at the envelope and unfolded the thin sheet.

At first the words were meaningless, clumped together, indistinguishable. She read them again. Then she screamed. It was only a small scream. But it was joyous! It turned into laughter, then laughter to tears. She ran into the bedroom and snatched up the baby. He blinked at her, wide-eyed; he puckered his face and smiled. She whirled around the room with him once; she hugged him.

"Alexander, Alexander, your father's alive! Do you understand, do you understand, my darling? He's alive, and we're going to see him, you and I."

She dropped to her knees, still holding the baby. The miracle had happened! She had been right. She had walked by faith, and that faith had been rewarded.

She rocked the baby, back and forth, there on her knees. *So there is a tomorrow in my life!* She hugged him to her, fearful of the joy that swept the cobwebs of longing from her heart and dissolved the dark pain she had lived with so long a time!

*   *   *   *   *   *

"I'll do whatever you recommend, sir," she told the doctor.

David Russell liked the serene, intelligent look in her eyes. He studied the question a moment.

"It's hard to guess at. It could go either way, you know."

"Let's take a chance," she said. Were her dark eyes sparkling?

"It may be hell for you, my dear," he replied.

"I know. How well I know!" Her laugh held a shudder. "But it may be just what Adam Hutton needs."

Dr. Russell smiled. "All right, let's try it. I'll have Maria take your bags up to the house."

"Now, Alex, Alex! Take me to Alexander!"

David Russell grinned this time. "This way," he said.

Julia hated the smell of hospitals, bitter and sterile. This was worse than any she had seen. The patients here were so quiet, so sick, so wounded. They led her to a door. She pushed it aside.

A man lay on the bed. Her heart stopped beating. The patterns from the early-morning sun scattered bright jewels of light about him. He lay very still, not even the patterns were moving. There was a bandage wrapped around his head.

She moved a step or two forward. She couldn't see him, couldn't see his face; the face was turned aside. She hesitated and looked back at the doctor.

"It's all right. Go ahead," he nodded.

She moved to the bed. The arm outside the covers was Alex's arm. The hand, so slender and sinewy, always so warm, so warm on hers! She touched the quiet hand. The head turned slowly. The bandages didn't matter, the poorly-shaven stubble, the sallow skin. This was Alex! With a cry, she bent and kissed him. His eyelids flickered. She smoothed his cheek with her hand. The eyelids flickered again, but they didn't open. Julia looked back at the doctor questioningly.

"I'm afraid he's unconscious. He floats in and out rather

quickly. It's difficult to anticipate."

"May I be with him alone for awhile, anyway?"

"Yes, of course. It surely can't hurt." He smiled at her kindly. "We're hoping it may even help."

He left the room, closing the door softly behind him.

Julia sat beside Alex for hours and talked to him softly, telling him all that had happened the last few months. She bent down beside him and told him some of her feelings, told him about the baby and touched his face. The eyelids never flickered again. When she rose to leave, she bent and kissed him.

"Sleep and get better, Alex. I'll be back."

She could be patient now; she knew so much about patience. And she knew, at this point, that their struggle was not alone. With that assurance, how could she doubt and be fearful?

Maria had taken the baby home with her luggage. Julia called a cab that would take her there. She was tired, and her body ached all over. But she was anxious to be with little Alexander again.

Point Charlotte, the house named for Alex's mother. They had transferred Adam there a few days before, set up with a day nurse, a night nurse, his own equipment—specialized around-the-clock care. Dr. Russell seemed to think he was gaining quickly.

"He's a tough old coot, and the crisis is definitely over. Maybe what he needs now is something to think about, something to draw him out of himself."

So she and the doctor were taking the chance together,

esconsing herself and the baby there. As the doctor said, the first few hours would tell it. What would happen—well, that was anybody's guess.

When she arrived at the house, both the baby and Adam were sleeping. She took a cool shower and changed into fresh, light clothes. Informed by Maria that there were some gentlemen to see her, she went hesitantly down to Adam's office, trembling a little to think of her last session there, but curious to see what the gentlemen wanted.

They represented the law firm of *Bailey, MacGregor & Bailey,* Adam's attorneys for the past twenty years. She smiled to herself when she realized they were assuming that Hutton family relationships were normal and smooth. They had some papers and documents to give her, things they felt ought to be explained. They seemed relieved she was here. It wouldn't hurt her to learn a thing or two from them. She greeted them warmly, inviting them to proceed.

Early that evening she ate a light, lovely dinner and played with the baby, then dialed Dr. Russell. He reassured her again that he would call her the first time Alex regained consciousness, no matter when. She hesitated, then proceeded with her second reason for calling.

"I've a hunch, Dr. Russell. I don't know if you'll agree. But is there any way you could do away with the night nurse?"

He laughed. "Rope or candlestick? Or ought we to simply use drugs?"

Julia laughed in return, then explained to him her reasons. He thought as he listened, *This is one very sharp girl!*

"I think that will work. Let me speak to the nurse first. And you get thorough instructions from her before she leaves."

210

Two hours later, still too early for bed, Julia sat in her room writing a note to her parents, trying to untangle the events of the past few days. She heard the heavy breathing, the shuffled walking. She looked up; Adam Hutton stood hunched and glowering in her doorway.

"Ought you to be up and about?" she asked with concern.

He had a stout cane; he leaned on it heavily.

"That's no concern of yours, girl. Just what are you doing?"

"Writing to my mother," she answered demurely.

"Very clever, Julia, but you know that isn't the question. Just what in the hell are you doing in my house?"

Even hunched, even shrunken and sick, he was still imposing. His voice was still cold with authority and disdain.

"I am here by invitation, Adam Hutton. And . . ."

"Not by my invitation," he roared, and his face went pale.

Julia rose, a little alarmed.

"Please, don't get excited. It will do you more harm than good this time."

He pointed a finger at her, a long, slender finger.

"I will not endure this impunity. You will leave. You will learn . . ."

"I'm terribly sorry, Adam. But I shall not leave, and I shall not put up with your ravings."

She walked closer to him. His breathing was labored now. But his eyes, the deep-set eyes, were dark and blazing.

"Your memory has failed you, Adam. Let me refresh it. Alex turned twenty-five in January, didn't he?"

Adam growled under his breath, and Julia hurried on.

"We had been married nearly five months at that time, Adam. And if you recall, I was then alone in Utah and Alex thousands of miles from here fighting a war."

"What you getting at?" he grumbled.

He moved heavily and eased himself down on a chair. As he did so, Julia turned to the small French secretary in the corner, drew out some papers, and then approached him again.

"It was your own arrangement, Adam. And very good thinking."

She spread out the documents she held in her hand.

"The deed to Point Charlotte, Adam, that passed to Alex—provided he was married—at age twenty-five. The terms of the trust that you set up yourself, Adam—so the ownership passes to Alex . . . and Alex's wife."

He muttered under his breath; she couldn't quite hear him, though she had the impression he was calling her ugly names.

Damn, he thought to himself, *how did I overlook that? It was meant to be Alex and Lillian, never this little witch!*

Julia watched him carefully for signs of danger. After a moment or two he regained control.

"Very clever, my dear. You think you have things sewed up here."

He lowered his brow and scowled like a trapped, angry bear, all venom and hatred. Julia felt her skin prickle.

"I see I shall have to endure your impertinence now. I am helpless to do otherwise."

He spread out his hands and laughed the short, ugly laugh that Julia hated.

"But, ah! I have a reason to live and fight now. I've a trick or two left in my bag, don't doubt it, my girl!"

Julia trembled. Was what he was saying only bravado? There could still be so many things she didn't know! He struggled to rise; she moved and bent to help him. As her fingers touched his arm, he wrenched away.

"Don't you presume to weaken me further, Julia. I came

here on my own powers, I'll return the same way."

"Proud and cold and empty. Right, Adam? Even death couldn't teach you anything. Something to live for! The same old, empty hatred, the same pathetic—"

The sharp cry startled them both. It came from the nursery, the small room adjoining hers.

"Alexander," Julia whispered. She smiled, her eyes glowing. "Come and see him."

She reached for his arm, but he drew away. She searched his eyes; the heavy eyes were veiled now.

"Please," she said softly. "It's your blood runs in his veins. That ought to convince you to at least give the boy a chance."

She turned and crossed the room, her heart beating quickly, barely breathing until she heard his following tread. It took him so long to cross the few yards to the doorway.

When he came in the door, she had the small table lamp lit, and Alexander lay uncovered, awake and kicking. She turned away and fussed with some things on the dresser.

Slowly Adam Hutton approached the bed. She could hear Alexander coo; she hoped he was smiling. *Please smile at your wretched old grandfather,* she said to herself. *Go on, Alexander, twist his old heart a little.*

She turned back softly, barely making a sound. Adam's long, thin finger was clasped in Alexander's small fist. The little round eyes were bubbling over with laughter.

"He looks very much like Alex looked at this age."

Julia's heart was fluttering wildly in her breast.

"I thought he did, but I wasn't sure."

Alexander rocked and kicked and cooed and chattered, happy for company, oblivious to moods.

"Bright, isn't he?" Adam's voice was a little husky.

"Oh, yes, and so good-tempered!" Julia laughed, bright

and spontaneous, beautiful and rich. "In spite of being related to you," she added.

Adam glanced at her from the corner of his eye. He thought the girl looked even prettier than before. Glowing, somehow—motherhood did that for some women. It had with his Charlotte. He'd seen that look before.

"I'll be right back," Julia breathed as, suddenly, she left him. Adam looked behind to be certain; she was gone. He turned to the child.

"You're a prettier baby than Alex. Almost too pretty to be a boy."

Alexander smiled and pulled on the finger he held. Adam leaned close and stroked the flower-soft skin. *How long has it been since I touched a baby? Alex's baby! Son of my only son.*

A flood of unwanted emotion began to choke him. Suddenly Alex's death, the loss he'd thought real, loomed up like an old, black nightmare before his eyes. He had his son back! Alex was alive! There *was* something to live and plan for now. Alex . . . and this beautiful little mite she called Alexander.

Julia made plenty of noise. He heard her returning. He dashed the wet from his eye and softly disengaged his finger.

"Here's a picture of Alexander I thought you'd like, though you'll probably get more than enough of the real thing now."

Her voice held something happy and musical in it. It had been so long since he'd heard that kind of a voice! Before he could protest she stuck the photo into the pocket of his robe. Then she took his arm. She was stronger than he had imagined.

"I'll have no nonsense," she said, "I'm helping you back to your room."

He didn't protest. He knew he couldn't make it. His muscles felt too watery and weak. They didn't speak, but when they reached his door, she darted inside and straightened and smoothed his bedcovers, refilled the glass of water beside his bed, did half a dozen things in as many minutes, and the room had the sudden look of a woman's touch. She smiled.

"I think that will do. Pleasant dreams, Adam."

Ever so quickly, so briefly, she touched his hand; then she was gone. He lay there, looking after her.

"That's a damn underhanded tactic," he muttered. "Win me with kindness—weaken me, she would!"

In spite of his grumblings, he knew it wasn't a tactic. It had been a long, long time, but he knew how to feel, how to recognize genuine tenderness in a woman. He lay back against the pillows, but he didn't sleep yet. He drew out the picture and studied the features of the beautiful child and thought deep thoughts long into the night.

Nor the god of war shall seize this prey
Out of his father's hands: Our wars are done.
Know, my hearts, I hope well of tomorrow . . . . .
SHAKESPEARE

_____ **16**

E arly the next morning, before Julia could quite get her bearings, Maria informed her that Dr. Russell was at the door. Julia went down eagerly. No, he told her, there was no change in Alex.

"That's what I've come to discuss," he said. "Though, by the way, how are you getting on with Adam?"

She gave him a brief report, and they decided to carry on.

"I hope you can stand that pressure along with all the rest."

All the rest, of course, meant Alex. Julia smiled.

"I'll just have to," she said.

They went up together to Adam, and Dr. Russell explained the procedures he recommended.

"Alex is suffering," he explained, "from a subdural hematoma with some probable associated cerebral edema."

It sounded serious to Julia, and it was, especially with his other associated injuries.

"This condition," the doctor went on, "puts pressure on the brain. Yet, in spite of that, it can sometimes be very subtle and not show itself in initial examinations. They obviously suspected but did not discover it in Hawaii."

He went on to explain the more technical conditions: the

collection of blood underneath the dura, the gradual formation of a membrane and the fluid build-up within the membrane walls. It was difficult for Julia to follow. She was more concerned about what had to be done to correct the condition.

"We call it trephining," Dr. Russell told her. "We drill small burr holes to relieve the pressure. We hope this will alleviate the headaches, the unconsciousness, and the impaired vision. Perhaps even the memory will improve."

He went on to explain more details about the procedure and to inform them that the operation was set for the following morning.

"That's the soonest we can schedule the O.R.," he told them. "And I'd like Dr. Grant to assist me."

Julia walked the doctor to the door.

"I'm not sure I want Alex to see you now," Dr. Russell said. "Even if he becomes conscious and lucid. Right before the operation he needs to be calm. Tomorrow, afterward, it will be much better."

Julia swallowed and nodded.

"Perhaps if he's still unconscious I could come for awhile. Tonight. Just to say . . . hello."

Dr. Russell nodded. "I'll call you," he promised.

Julia was thinking she'd arrange for the elders to administer to Alex. But she didn't need to mention that to the doctor now and certainly not to Adam.

She said good-bye. When he left, the whole house seemed empty. It was going to be a very long day.

Going back up the stairs she could see that Adam was out walking along the easy path by the sea. The day nurse was with him. Julia ran out, down the pebbled path, and came up behind them.

"That will be all, Miss Miller," she said brightly. "I'll accompany Mr. Hutton the rest of the way."

Adam grunted but didn't forbid it. The nurse stepped back and aside. Julia fitted her stride to Adam's and took a deep breath.

"It's a beautiful morning. How can it be so lovely when people are suffering, struggling between life and death?"

He didn't reply. They walked a few moments in silence.

"Do you love the sea? I suppose it could be a great solace. It can match you for intensity at least!"

Adam grunted again. "It's an improvement over corn fields," he said.

Her musical laugh rang out, lilting and gentle.

"Oh, I don't know about that. I love the corn fields. The wind that makes the corn leaves squeak when they're moist and green, then rattles them like dead ghosts when the autumn has dried them."

He glanced at her out of the corner of his eye.

"But the ocean. The ocean gets into your very soul."

Her eyes were wide and shining, flecked with color. They came to a bench, and Adam sat heavily down.

"I want the nurse," he said. "Go back and get her."

"I can help you," Julia began. But he waved his hand.

"I don't want you here. Now do as I tell you, woman."

She stood a moment, regarding him seriously.

"Adam, I suppose in five lifetimes you'd never believe this. But I don't want to be your enemy."

He looked away, but he didn't interrupt her.

"'After that operation tomorrow, what then? Alex will need a lot of love and help. Do you think he deserves to come home to unkindness and hatred? Do you suppose that's what will help him get well?"

He didn't reply or acknowledge that he had heard her.

"He deserves much more from both of us," she cried. "And you know it."

He sat like stone. She was close to crying. She turned on her heel and left him.

You're a fool, she berated herself, *a foolish child to believe you can change a man like that.*

Julia had a quiet dinner with Alexander. The hours were cruel; the hours dragged by too slowly. She hadn't seen Adam again all day. A little later Maria came looking for her. Her face appeared a bit white and distressed.

"Mr. Hutton wishes to see you immediately."

That sounded like a summons, not something the matter. Julia went to his bedroom. The door was opened wide. His huge, four-poster bed was scattered with papers. Papers and folders and ledgers spread here and there.

"All right, Julia, just what in the hell have you been up to?"

She blinked a little. "I beg your pardon," she said.

He swore again under his breath.

"I have my network. My network still functions," he growled, "whether I do or not. I have just been informed that my man, Clarence Johnson, is back in California."

So that was it!

"Did you hear me, girl? He's back making nasty noises about some business of firing him on the spot, no chance to explain, no benefits, no fair treatment—"

"That's hogwash!" Julia interrupted indignantly. "He ought to be more than fired, Adam Hutton. You and your 'network' ought to prosecute him as well. You wait right here."

She dashed off, but was back in a minute with her own fat folder. She laid it on Adam's lap.

"All the facts and figures are there. Go ahead, look at them. You'll see in a moment what kind of stuff Johnson's been pulling."

"Meaning the man's been fooling me all these months? And I didn't have enough sense to see it?"

He was getting red in the face.

"Calm down," Julia warned him. "You said it, I didn't. Go ahead, look, if you dare."

"Mrs. Hutton!" The nurse, alarmed, was tugging at her. Adam was pulling himself up on the pillows, his face still red.

"Just who do you think you are?" he bellowed. "Using my name. Usurping authority. Taking over one of my plants?"

He had grown quite breathless. Julia drew herself up straight. Her eyes were flashing.

"Just who do I think I am?" she repeated. "I am Julia Hutton, Adam. And don't you forget it."

"You're a cur, a usurper. You are *not* a Hutton!" he yelled, enraged. "Just what were your motives, anyway? To make me a laughingstock, to undermine me, to . . ."

"No!" She shouted back. She was trembling. "No, you fool. I'm not as wretched as you are!"

Adam was breathing heavily, his eyes dark with anger and pain. She glared at the dark eyes, her own eyes filling with tears.

"All right, Adam. I'll tell you why I did it. To please you! To make you proud of me for once."

She wiped at the tears that were spilling from her eyes now.

"Pathetic, yes, I know. Well, go ahead, laugh. Gloat a little. I did it to win your praise, to make you accept me—to prove that I am a Hutton once and for all!"

With a little sob she turned and ran from the bedroom. Adam's head was spinning; he felt as weak as a baby. He fell back against the pillows and closed his eyes. The nurse, that stupid, awkward nurse, started fussing around him, gathering up his papers. He clutched at the folder, the one that Julia had given him.

"Get out of here. I'm all right," he sputtered. "And leave these things where they are. Out! Out, I said!"

The nurse obeyed, thinking, *Let the old tyrant die, then!* She had never met such a hard, distasteful man.

Julia was back in her room, preparing to cry her heart out, when the telephone rang. She picked up her extension. Dr. Russell's voice came over the line. It was seven o'clock. She'd entirely forgotten!

Yes, she would be there in half an hour she told him. No, she wouldn't stay for long she promised. She had already asked the elders to come at eight. She rushed to comb her hair and repair her make-up and check on Alexander before she left.

Adam heard the car pull out of the driveway. He wished he was going with her to see his boy. He cursed the flabby weakness of his muscles, the pain that kept returning in his chest. What a cruel and heartless enemy weakness was! *How could he let Alex see him like this!*

There were tears in his eyes, tears of angry frustration! He opened the folder that still lay in his lap. *Let's see what in the hell Julia's been up to!*

Alex wasn't conscious, but Julia sat beside him and held his hand and talked to him quietly. She whispered into his ear how much she loved him and about the wonderful son he was going to see. Somewhere down inside a fear was building. He was so close—and yet not here at all! What if they rolled him in for the operation and he peacefully, quietly slipped away?

She had never doubted before, and that alone scared her. Perhaps it was just what she'd been through the last few days. She'd been thinking of Alex and Adam and Alexander—everyone's needs except her own. She wanted to shake the still, unresponsive body. She wanted to scream at him, "Alex, I need you, now!"

The reality of that need swept like ice water through her. Without Alex how could she live—how could she go on?

After the elders came, it seemed a little better. Some of the warmth and peace flowed back into her soul. She remembered again there were higher ways than her ways, wiser powers than hers to carry this through.

She left the hospital, but she hated to go back yet. She drove beside the seashore, then stopped the big car and walked along a lonely stretch of sand, taking off shoes and stockings to wade in the water, feeling the waves curl up around her knees, wetting the hem of her dress and cooling her skin. The warm night, the whispering sea combined to soothe her, to make her feel clean and whole again.

The hours had passed slowly for Adam. He knew Julia wasn't supposed to visit long. What was she doing, anyway?

He had read through her papers and records with fascination. After a glance or two, he had known she was right. But some of the things she and Clayton concocted! He couldn't believe the business head she had.

It was brilliant how they had taken on this order, organized and pulled the whole thing off. He was impressed by how careful she'd been of every detail, giving him an accounting he couldn't fault. Then before she had come out here to California, she'd made Oscar Clayton manager in Johnson's stead. Adam seemed to recall that's what Alex had wanted him to do in the first place. But, of course, he could never have given in to that!

Adam sighed. He kept the bedside lamp still burning. He was determined to wait up until she came back.

Julia swept the big car along the wide, curved driveway. It was eleven o'clock; she hadn't realized it was so late. She parked the car and walked up to the house. She hoped little Alexander was asleep.

Adam heard her coming. He lay back into the pillows and closed his eyes. Now that she was actually here what good did it do him? What excuse could he use to call her? What could he say? He felt stranded and helpless and out of his element.

Julia paused at the top of the stairs. The house was so quiet. She could see the thin line of light under Adam's door. She turned in that direction and pushed the door gently. He was lying against the pillows. His eyes were closed.

She took a few steps, paused, then a few steps further.

"Adam?" She barely breathed the word. He stirred a little, but his eyes didn't open.

"I . . . I just thought I'd let you know I was back . . . and see if you were all right."

There was silence a moment.

"How is Alex?" The words were quiet, the eyes were still closed.

"The same I guess. Resting. All right."

She paused in the silence.

"I don't know—I don't know," she said softly. "It's so eerie seeing him lying there that way. So still, so hurt, so unresponsive."

She could hear the tick of the grandfather clock in the upstairs hallway. It was so very quiet. She could hear Adam's labored breath. She moved slowly until she stood very close to the bed.

"Adam," she said softly. "I just wanted to tell you, before tomorrow . . . before . . . I just want you to know."

She took a deep breath, a woman's soft breath in the stillness, as sweet as the sound of the sea, of the sigh of the wind.

"I love him, I love him so deeply, Adam! I won't hurt him or fail him, as you've been hurt and failed. I won't run away like my mother—and I won't die."

She was crying, gentle tears, and her voice was gentle.

"I'll love him and stand beside him the rest of his life."

She paused; she backed away. He was holding his breath now. Then suddenly she was beside him again.

"Please, Adam, try!" Her voice was a painful whisper. "Please give life just one more chance. I know how much pain there can be in loving. But you've got to, Adam, for your own sake, you've got to. In order to be a man again!"

She was much too close. He could feel his insides trembling. Her fragrance was in his nostrils, her hand on his arm.

"You can love Alex and trust him. You know that, Adam." Her voice grew small; he could barely hear her voice. "You can trust me and love me, too, Adam . . . you can."

Her hair fell over his arm, her sweet breath touched him. Gentle lips pressed briefly against his cheek. Then she turned and was gone. There was nothing but his own breathing—painful, oh, so painful, against his chest.

224

The tears were hot in his eyes, but he didn't stop them. He hadn't cried since the day that Charlotte died. *If only she were here right now to hold him!*

He cried as he had often wanted to cry. And he longed, as he had often longed, for a woman. In his cold, bitter loneliness he cried, facing himself alone in the awful darkness, with no one to help him and no place where he could hide.

It was a long and grueling ordeal which began the next morning. Julia went early to the hospital, but Dr. Russell insisted that Adam rest at home as long as he could.

"There's really nothing either of you can do here for hours," he told them.

But Julia felt better being there, close by.

The operation passed; the physicians called it successful. Alex was safe in recovery now. Julia ate a little lunch, called to check on the baby, then went back to waiting.

But there was a difference. She felt a certain hopeful impatience, as though she could see a light at the end of the tunnel, as though there was really something to wait for now.

Three hours in recovery. Alex was conscious! They wheeled him into his own private room. The doctors checked him over; the nurses checked him. They gave him a little while longer to rest. Dr. Russell called the house. The old chauffeur brought the nurse, Maria, Adam, and Alexander at last!

Adam looked a little rough when Julia saw him; his eyes were red. He seemed older suddenly. Or perhaps it was just the uncertain air about him, something so very alien to the man.

Dr. Russell came up and explained a few things to them.

"Well," he said at last, spreading his hands. "Alex knows you're out here. You may as well not keep him waiting."

He smiled. Julia reached out and grasped his hand. Her

eyes were shining, something inside her was singing.

"I'm terrified," she whispered. He patted her hand.

She started walking. She could hear Adam behind her. They hadn't really spoken since he arrived. Before he really stumbled, Julia sensed it. She heard the sharp scrape of the cane on the polished linoleum floor. In an instant she was beside him, supporting his body. He leaned against her; she felt his hand on her arm.

"Don't be afraid," she whispered against his ear.

He looked at her, with deep and steady eyes.

"It's you Alex will be wanting," he told her. "It's your place beside him. I'll wait here with the child."

She stared back at him, almost uncomprehending. He nodded.

"Go on now." His voice—did his voice sound kind?

She walked the interminable distance to the door. Silently she pushed it and walked inside. There was no still form lying against the pillows, no silent, unmoving shadow to greet her now. Alex was sitting, propped up, waiting for her.

The first thing Julia saw were his beautiful eyes, warm and deep and filling with light as he saw her. For a moment she stood there, frozen within his gaze. Then, with a cry, she was beside him. She felt his hand—the gentle, sinewy fingers twine themselves into her hair. She felt his lips on her cheek, on her eyes, on her own lips. She kissed him until she couldn't breathe.

She drew back. The red-brown eyes were alive and smiling. He spoke her name again and again. His voice was like a current running through her, agonizing, thrilling, and sweet.

He thought as he gazed at her face, at her aching perfection, *As long as I live, I'll never forget this sight, this feeling of joy, this love that fills me.*

She could scarcely breathe, she was laughing and crying

226

together. He pulled her down beside him. She felt the beating of his heart. She whispered against his ear, "I love you, Alex. A lifetime with you won't begin to be enough."

"I intend to hold you to your initial bargain, Julia." His voice was husky. "Forever. Remember, my love?"

My love, my love! The words went singing through her.

"Alex," she cried out, "there's somebody you must see!" She rose and turned, then twirled again to face him.

"There are actually two people waiting. Two people who love you."

She flung open the door.

"Adam! Where are you, Adam?"

She found him. She tugged at his arm. Her eyes were glowing.

"Where is my baby?"

Maria hurried forward. Julia took her son and placed the wide-eyed bundle in Adam's arms.

"I think you ought to be the one to take him."

Adam eyed her. She smiled back at the deep, dark eyes.

"You'll have to help me walk then; he's quite an armful."

Julia smiled. She took his arm; she found his hand.

"Why not?" Adam snorted. "He's a Hutton, isn't he?"

It was a challenge. Julia nodded.

"Yes, sir. He's a Hutton through and through."

They reached the door. Julia pushed it and held it for him. There was something moist and sparkling in his eyes. He dropped her hand, but before he dropped it he squeezed it. His voice, when it came, was husky but warm. Warm and wonderful!

"After you," he bellowed. "After you, Mrs. Hutton."

Julia gazed into the deep, amazing eyes. She knew she

would never see hatred there again. She knew that, somehow, the miracle was complete.

"Please, Adam," Julia whispered, "let's go together."

He didn't even hesitate. He wrapped his big, bear arm around her shoulders, and walked in with her to the son he loved.